S0-CBN-051

ROY ARONSON

Arrowvet Publishers

Arrowvet Publishers;
always on target

Copyright © Arrowvet Publishers 2007
Copyright © text: Roy Aronson
Contact: roy@citivet.co.za
Publishing manager: Lindsay Norman, Quick Brown Fox
Designer: Patricia Lynch Blom patz@zeplins.co.za
Illustrations: Lexie Aronson
Cover photograph: Nikki Bartlet
Dedication photograph: Nikki Bartlet
Printed and bound by Creda Communications

All rights reserved. No part of this publication may be reproduced, stored
in a retrieval system, or transmitted, in any form or any means, electronic,
mechanical, photocopying, recording or otherwise, without the prior written
permission of the copyright owner.

ISBN: 978-0-2040-0196-6

CONTENTS

I wish to dedicate this book to the following:

My colleagues, the veterinarians wherever they are in the
world, especially the wonderful vets in South Africa. Vets are the true
health professionals in the animal world.

This wonderful land that I live in called South Africa

The beautiful open spaces that are wild life reserves

The animals, my patients, my teachers

My family

JABU

I LOOKED UP, drenched to the skin and, not for the first time, realised that even baby elephants can be dangerous. When I first met Jabu, he was just a baby of two, albeit a very big one. He weighed in at some six hundred kilograms but still had that cuddly sort of appearance that all infant animals have. I think it has something to do with the fact that their eyes are relatively large for their heads. This gives them the sort of endearing appearance that infants have. His ears were also large so what with big eyes and big ears and a trunk that appeared a little too short for his head, we had a cuddly little elephant that everyone wanted to pet. But even though this little animal was only two years' old and semi hand-reared, he was still a wild African elephant.

WE HAD A CUDDLY LITTLE ELEPHANT THAT EVERYONE WANTED TO PET.

Jabu's handler was Willem and they both lived at the "Cheetah Project" on Kapama Game Reserve. Willem was graphic testimony to the fact that even at two years of age and looking very cute, a baby elephant still presents potential for great danger and injury. A few months before I met Jabu, Willem had had his nose and arm broken when Jabu, in his excitement at greeting Willem, accidentally ran right over him. Six hundred kilograms of baby elephant is a lot of elephant and can do a lot of damage even if unintentional. Since then Willem adopted a different tack and now carries a special mahouts rod that he uses to guide Jabu. He also makes sure that if Jabu comes straight at him he moves over to one side so that he is not bowled over by the enthusiastic baby again.

Tales of an African Vet

DROUGHT IS ALWAYS A HARD TIME FOR THE ANIMALS OF THE AFRICAN PLAINS. THEY RELY ON THE RAIN.

I had the opportunity to meet Jabu and water him at the end of the day, giving him a running hose that he placed into his mouth and, with loud slurping sounds, he filled his belly with all the water he needed. Once he had had enough water it was playtime. He had learned to hold the hose with the tip of his trunk and he was then able to thoroughly drench all of us standing around him. As I said, baby elephants can be very dangerous.

This is Jabu's story.

The long shadows of dusk cast themselves over the dry plains of Africa as the setting sun sunk low over the horizon.

The day was near its end. It was a warm evening in early autumn. Summer had not seen a lot of rain despite the area being a summer rainfall one. The earth was dry and dusty and the grasses were starting to turn yellow at their tips. It would be a dry winter that year and following on a dry summer, conditions in the bush were not looking promising. Drought is always a hard time for the animals of the African plains. They rely on the rain. Rain brings life to the grasses and the grazers prosper. The predators who feed off the grazers also prosper. But without rain, all the animals suffer.

The water pans and dams were much dryer than they should have been. The approaches to the water holes are usually surrounded by hard compact earth from the many feet and hooves that trample the earth. This hard compacted earth ends at the water. The transition from earth to dam is sudden and the fringe of soft mud surrounding the body of water is usually quite small. When the rains are scarce and the air and the earth are dry, the mud fringe expands. As the water recedes, the muddy zone can increase dramatically. Conditions that year were such that the mud zone was at its maximum.

If you are a large three-ton elephant, this presents no problem at all. In fact, the mud zone is a favoured area – a wallow in which to coat your hard tough hide with mud. Once the mud dries, you can scrape your body against a rough tree and all those parasites that stick to your skin will be rubbed off, giving you blessed relief. For a little baby elephant, however, the mud zone can be a death trap.

Jabu was three months old. He was born at the beginning of summer, which is usually an excellent time to be born. But this year things were a little different. The rains were early and light. The plains had enough water to provide grass for his mother to eat but not in abundance. Still, she was able to provide him with the rich milk that he needed to ensure that he grew at the normal rate. He looked like all baby elephants do at that age – adorable. His little body seemed too small for his big head. His little trunk seemed too small for his body and his eyes, like

HE WAS BORN INTO AN EXTENDED FAMILY.

all baby eyes, were large and liquid with long eyelashes. His ears, those wonderful bush air conditioners provided for him by Mother Nature, flapped constantly, keeping him cool through the long hot summer. Within a few hours of being born he was on his feet and able to walk and keep up with his mother. He was born into an extended family. His mother had three aunties who assisted her in the birth. These three female elephants took their duties very seriously and kept guard during the birthing process. Once he was born they assisted wherever they could. They fussed over him and ensured that he kept pace when they were walking. When he played, someone always kept an eye on him. If predators were around then the three females plus his mother made a formidable team. The four of them formed a large impenetrable gray wall of African elephant behind which he could hide in safety. Altogether things in the early stage of a baby elephant's life were safe and favorable.

The four female elephants and their small charge soon joined the main herd again. The herd consisted of about a hundred animals. There were adult females and the younger animals were both male and female. The younger animals were all offspring of the females in the herd. As soon as a male became sexually mature he left the breeding herd to join the bachelor male herd. All the animals in the herd at present were either female or sexually immature males. This is how an elephant herd is structured.

The matriarch of the herd was a wise old female who had lived through more than forty summers. She knew the area of her domain well. She was concerned that year because there was simply not enough rain in the summer. The herd would have to move a little earlier that year. She had lived through drought before and knew what to do. Towards the end of February they would start their trek to areas where man had drilled wells into the earth and windmills pumped the precious water out of the deep places underneath the dry earth and into large concrete containers. These containers were high but presented no great challenge to an animal measuring over three metres at the withers and having a mobile trunk that could reach a further three metres.

HERD ON THE MOVE.

She did not know it was the 20th of February when she marshaled her herd and, via a series of infrasound communications, she managed to convey her message to them. It was time to move and she was setting the example by moving off first. The herd was used to her leadership and without much questioning they accepted her lead.

The three auntie females and the mother and their little elephant were concerned about the migration. The baby was only three months old and would be hard pressed to keep up with a herd that could walk comfortably at twelve kilometers an hour for the entire day. They may have to slow down in order to accommodate their little charge but in this event, they would easily be able to follow the path left by the migrating herd. The four of them were also up to the task of defending themselves so altogether there should have been no problem. If they arrived at their destination a few days or even a week or two late, they would be able to join the herd and see the dry months through where the matriarch chose.

It is a magnificent site to see the largest land mammals on the move. Their routine was inherited via genetic memory. They grazed and rested during the day. If they found water along the way, they drank their fill and if there was mud to

wallow in, they did this as well. During the cool of the early mornings and the late afternoons they traveled most of their journey. Dusk and dawn would find these large animals moving silently through the bush. It is amazing that nearly one hundred massive animals can move through the bush so quietly that if

A QUICK DRINK FROM HIS MOTHER DID MUCH TO FORTIFY HIM.

you did not see them, you would not know they were there. You might possibly hear the creak of a branch as it bends with their passage or the snap of a twig underfoot. If you listened very carefully you might hear a soft rustle. These gentle sounds belie the size of the migration. In the late afternoon the sun caused the dust surrounding these moving giants to glow red. In this reddish glow the silhouettes of these majestic animals moved quietly towards their destination.

The baby elephant was managing the journey so far. He was foot sore and felt a little lightheaded but a quick drink from his mother did much to fortify him. His three aunties

were there to assist as well and they made sure that the small group of travelers did not lag too far behind. Still, by the end of the first week they were about one day's march behind the main herd.

Dawn on the ninth day of their journey found the small group of four adult elephants and one baby marching with purpose in the direction of the rest of the herd. It was cool and they had been on the move since long before dawn. The air was still and the promise of a hot day ahead of them made the adults decide to press on till they came to water. The mother thought that she could smell water not far ahead. Only an hour or two until they got there. In her distant memory she also had the faint remnants of vague recognition of where she was and she was fairly sure that there was water ahead. Their march would take them until just after sunrise but the promise of a cool drink and even a wallow was tempting beyond belief.

Sure enough, within the space of two hours they arrived at the edge of a water hole. It is usually large and filled with an abundance of fresh clear water but due to the scarcity of rain, it was different this year. There was still water and enough to drink but the border of the water hole was soft treacherous mud. The fringe of mud must have been ten metres wide. If you are an adult elephant the mud was of no consequence but to a three month old baby, it was lethal.

The adults realised the problem but just too late to stop the little one from rushing with a squeal of delight towards the water and the mud. With horror they watched as their precious baby ran towards the thick black sludge. His momentum took him through the first five metres and then he stuck fast.

THE AIR WAS STILL AND THE PROMISE OF A HOT DAY AHEAD OF THEM MADE THE ADULTS DECIDE TO PRESS ON TILL THEY CAME TO WATER.

Initially he did not realise what had happened and his efforts to take him to the water churned up the mud even further and caused him to sink in to the bottom of his belly. Only then did the little baby go quiet and this enabled him to hear the calls of warning issued by his mother and aunts. His mother signaled for him to keep still. This was a signal he knew well. Many times it was issued to him if a predator was close by. Instantly he obeyed this command. His mother lumbered up close to him and his aunties stood back allowing the mother to survey the problem and try and plan their next move. If they had hands they could have just lifted him out of the mud but elephants are unable to lift their young. Despite their vast strength their trunks are not designed for this task. They can push and pull but they cannot lift their young.

The mother enjoined her baby to be still and tried to wrap her trunk round his little head in order to pull him. As soon as she exerted pressure, he squealed in pain. Clearly this would not work. She tried to use her trunk to push him from behind but all this did was to drive his little head towards the mud. They then tried to encourage him to thrash about himself whilst the adults pushed and pulled at the same time but this too did not work. By now the little animal was buried half way up his belly. He was terrified for his life. The adults stood back to survey their predicament. His mother once again gave him the signal to stand still and he once again obeyed her. He indicated that he was hot and thirsty and the adults helped him by spraying water over him and the mother allowed him to drink. More than this they could not do. The knowledge that the little baby was doomed took its time to sink in. Slowly however they realized that he was trapped in the mud and there was nothing they could do. The small herd stayed

THE MOTHER TRIED TO WRAP HER TRUNK ROUND HIS LITTLE HEAD IN ORDER TO PULL HIM.

VULTURES WERE CIRCLING OVERHEAD INDICATING A KILL.

together for the day and gave the baby shelter from the sun and kept him cool by dowsing him with water but as the cool of the evening approached, the powerful instinct of survival that exists in animals started to come to the fore. Knowing that the young animal was doomed, the instinct for the adults to move along their journey became overwhelming. There was nothing more they could do for the baby.

It is a strange and marked difference between animals and man. Humans will sacrifice their lives in defense of their young. Many times in the animal world, the young fall prey to a predator. The adult will defend its young vigorously but not to the death. When all appears lost the adult will give up before death in order to survive and be able to procreate again. Survival of the species resides in the adults and yet the future of mankind rests in its youth.

Sadly and with great pain in their hearts the four adults started to move off in the dusk, leaving the terrified little elephant trapped firmly in the mud. They hoped in their hearts that the end would be swift and merciful.

And that was where he was found just about twelve hours later by a patrolling ranger whose dawn patrol took him near to the waterhole with the mud fringe containing the trapped little elephant.

Vultures were circling overhead indicating a kill. The ranger had spotted them in his early morning patrol and decided to have a look. His area of responsibility was vast, some fifty by fifty

kilometres, about two thousand five hundred square kilometres. This area of patrol was but a small speck in the vastness of the wildlife reserve that the elephants were migrating in.

The Kruger Park is some twenty thousand square kilometers in size. On its eastern borders, the Mozambique national park stretched for many thousands of square kilometers. The Lebombo Mountain range separated the two wilderness areas. On the western side of the park there were numerous private reserves such as the Timbavati reserve and the Klasseri reserve. The fences that used to separate these areas had long been removed and animals were now free to migrate along traditional routes used by their ancestors. In the future there is a trans frontier park proposed that will span the border between South Africa and Mozambique making this the largest contiguous wildlife reserve on the planet. These thoughts however were for the future, right now, the fate of our little elephant was in the hands of the game ranger who had stumbled onto him during his patrol.

The little elephant had walked into a muddy wallow near the small bushveld town of Hoedspruit. The wallow was in the Klasseri Reserve. With one glance the ranger took in the tragic situation. The circling vultures had not yet settled down to feed. The large footprints in the mud and the signs of the struggle told their eloquent story. He correctly surmised that the little elephant had got stuck and the adults had tried in vain to rescue him. Seeing that the situation was ultimately hopeless they eventually gave up and migrated on. How sad and cruel nature can be.

He drove his game vehicle to the edge of the mud hole to have a closer look. Not long now and the vultures would settle and feed off the carcass that remained.

Suddenly a large eye opened and blinked feebly in the morning light. The little trunk stirred pathetically looking for its mothers nipple situated between her front limbs, only to find nothing. The ranger was stunned. The little elephant was alive.

This was his territory and he decided immediately to try and save the little elephant. Time was not on his side, however. The first call he made was to his assistants to bring straps to

pull the baby elephant out of the mud. Next he made a call to Dr Rogers who was the wildlife vet that they used on the reserve. A few brief words were all that was needed to mobilise the rescue team.

SUDDENLY A LARGE EYE OPENED AND BLINKED FEEBLY IN THE MORNING LIGHT.

Within half an hour all the role players had assembled round the muddy trap. The rescue team now got to work. The baby was too weak to struggle so when the ranger approached with the large web belts that would be tied around him, all that the little elephant could do was to look fearfully at him and once again feebly wave his trunk.

Straps were secured round the baby's neck and, using his arms, the ranger was able to push a strap under the baby's front legs and around his chest. Once this had been accomplished the straps were secured to the tail bar of the game vehicle. Using its power as well as gentle traction by the ranger and his helper, the lethal mud started to release its grip on the once doomed young elephant.

HE WAS IN THAT STRANGE LIMBO BETWEEN LIFE AND DEATH IN THE VERY LITERAL SENSE.

When it was free of mud, the vet approached and decided that the little elephant needed intravenous fluids immediately. If he survived it would be a miracle but miracles often happen in the wild. Using one of the large ear veins to secure an intravenous line, Dr Rogers set up his fluid administration set. The baby weighed about one hundred and fifty kilograms by now and was severely dehydrated. The correct dose was worked out and the administration began. As the fluids flowed in the baby would immediately regain some of his strength so it was decided to sedate him in a short while, trying to synchronise his recovery with the sedation. It was also decided that the baby should be taken to the Cheetah Project and be hospitalised at the wildlife hospital run by Dr Rogers.

This decided, the elephant was loaded up into the game vehicle along with the fluid administration equipment and two handlers and driven to the Cheetah Project. From certain death the little baby had been brought back from the brink. His survival was still not assured but neither was his death. He was in that strange limbo between life and death in the very literal sense.

Nursing a baby elephant back to health is a full time job. The hospital staff had to keep the little fellow company twenty four hours a day, seven days a week. They named him Jabu, which means happiness. He was kept on rehydration fluids intravenously for twenty-four hours and then the drip line was removed. He seemed more stable and a little brighter. There were large areas of skin that had been damaged by his immersion in the mud for so long. These areas of damaged skin would however heal. He was given a course of antibiotics in case of infection and was treated for shock with a large dose of steroids. His intestinal flora, the normal natural bacteria inhabiting his gut, was the first area to be affected by stress. In order to treat this, a mixture of

correct bacteria seeded into a milk formula was given to him orally. He needed to be taught how to suckle from a bottle because he was not yet eating solids.

The next few days would be crucial in determining if Jabu would live or die. The hospital staff pulled out all the stops to give him the best chance of survival. Luckily the little elephant was small enough to be handled and with regular handling over the next few days, he became calmer as he got to know the nurses at the hospital.

There is a fine line between life and death in animals like Jabu after they had been through an ordeal like this. But sometime on the third day of his treatment at the hospital he crossed that line back to the safe side. His spirits rose, his appetite increased and it seemed as though he would in fact survive, much to the joy of all the hospital staff. His treatment was not complete and he would still have to stay in the hospital for another ten days or so but it was time to actually start making plans for his future. He and his species live a long time, sometimes up to sixty or seventy years. They also grow up to be very large (weighing tons) and so choosing a home for him that would be a permanent one was an important consideration. Everyone involved agreed that he should not have a temporary home – a permanent solution was needed.

Lente Roode was approached and asked if Jabu could make his home on Kapama, initially as part of the Cheetah Project and ultimately possibly as one of the elephants that would carry people round the reserve. This had been a project that had been proposed and possibly Jabu would be one of the animals trained to do this. She magnanimously agreed to the proposal and this is how Jabu became part of the Cheetah Project.

THE LITTLE ELEPHANT WAS SMALL ENOUGH TO BE HANDLED AND WITH REGULAR HANDLING OVER THE NEXT FEW DAYS, HE BECAME CALMER.

Baby elephants need company in order to survive and thrive. The herd usually forms this vital element of the baby's upbringing. From a very early age the adults instill discipline into young elephants. There are do's and don'ts that are enforced by the herd. Without this discipline, many orphan elephants raised in captivity by humans grow up to be juvenile delinquents with aberrant behavior. With this problem clearly in mind, the team at Kapama set about trying to instill discipline and enforce certain rules of behaviour that would if not prevent delinquency, at least mitigate against the worst vices that captive reared elephants acquire.

The first matter to attend to was the appointment of a permanent handler who would bond with the baby. A permanent handler must accept his or her responsibility but also has to be accepted by the baby. It is no use trying to foist an inappropriate person on a baby elephant. The match is very important for future behaviour. One or two people at the Cheetah Project volunteered but within a few days it was seen that they were unsuitable.

Willem was a student employed at the Cheetah Project during his holidays. He was approaching the end of his course on wildlife management and the little elephant seemed to have a strong affinity for him. Whenever Willem passed near little Jabu he became very excited. Willem was a soft-spoken gentle person who at the same time was physically very strong. Whenever he had the chance he used to pass by the elephant enclosure and always had time to stroke and talk to Jabu. Clearly this was a very good match and after some discussion at management level it was decided to offer Willem the post of caretaker for Jabu. Willem was about to write his final examinations and, if all went well he would be finished

FROM A VERY EARLY AGE THE
ADULTS INSTILL DISCIPLINE INTO
YOUNG ELEPHANTS.

HE WAS FED EVERY FOUR HOURS WITH A
MILK SUPPLEMENT.

within a month. He would then take up his post as Jabu's keeper. He jumped at the opportunity and agreed to start working as soon as his exams were successfully completed. Within a month he had passed his finals and was able to take up his permanent post at Kapama.

The baby elephant routine was established. He was still bottle-fed and had quickly learned how to suckle from the large bottle that was used to feed him. He was fed every four hours with a milk supplement specially designed for the needs of a rapidly growing elephant. The bottle feeding would be his sole source of nutrition until he was about six months old, at which point some solids would be introduced into his diet. This would be considered early in the wilds but in a human-reared situation it is acceptable. Thankfully the task of rearing a baby elephant was not virgin territory and the staff at the Cheetah Project had many cases of hand-reared elephants to refer to.

Jabu thrived and grew. His relationship with Willem flourished. The bond between them is a beautiful thing to see. It was established by Willem's commitment to the little elephant. For the first year of the relationship Willem slept in Jabu's enclosure. During the cold winter months they slept in a stable and often in the warm summer months they slept under the stars. When Jabu was considered old enough, Willem started to leave the little elephant alone for certain times during the day. This weaning process is similar to that which happens in the wild. At about one year of age the baby elephants start to venture a few hundred metres from the main

HIS PLAYFULNESS WITH THE HOSEPIPE, WHILST DRENCHING, WAS VERY ENDEARING.

herd and try to graze by themselves. This allowed Willem some time off. Every morning and every evening come rain or shine, Willem and Jabu went for a walk along the perimeter fence. This walk would sometimes take as long as an hour. This is an important part of the socialisation process and allows Jabu to see the world.

The day that I first saw Jabu, he and Willem were returning from their evening walk. Jabu was now two years old. He stood almost as tall as I was. His shoulder was just shorter than mine. He still had all the cuteness of a baby elephant but he weighed in at an impressive six hundred kilograms. His behavior was exemplary for an orphan elephant. He had been taught not to rush people and was gentle with them. His playfulness with the hosepipe, whilst drenching, was very endearing. He seemed to know that he was getting up to mischief but this small indulgence was permitted. Willem proudly showed off his scars and broken bones, which were mute testimony to the power of even so small an elephant. The scary thought was that he was still going to grow to at least six times his present size.

I have had the great pleasure of observing this little elephant grow over the last four years of my visits to the area. Because I am not there constantly I am able to perceive his growth. He was six years old at the time of writing this story and he is big. He is three quarters grown and probably weighs two thousand kilograms, which is two metric tons. He stands a good fifty centimetres higher at the shoulder than my head and he is very strong. He is not yet a delinquent and we all hope that he will not be one, but it is still too early to

WILLEM PROUDLY SHOWED OFF HIS SCARS AND BROKEN BONES, WHICH WERE MUTE TESTIMONY TO THE POWER OF EVEN SO SMALL AN ELEPHANT.

tell. Usually their aberrant behavior only starts to manifest at puberty, which is about ten to eleven years of age. The signs are good though, because some of specific behavior patterns that cause delinquency have been carefully avoided. The plans to 'back' him and use him as a riding elephant for game walks is still under consideration, but that will unfold in the future. For now Jabu is still in Willem's care and they still maintain their daily routine.

Jabu is a very important feature of life on Kapama. His story is all at once heartbreaking and heart-warming. I look forward to following his life story and meeting up with him when my work takes me to this wonderful part of the world.

1. *Willem and Jabu returning from a morning walk.*

2. *Jabu was half the size of this baby elephant when he was rescued from the mud.*

3. *My first meeting with Jabu. On my left is my friend Dr Peter Rogers, a specialist wildlife vet.*

A HEDGEHOG (in Latin *Erinaceus* sp.) – is a small ball of more than 7 000 spines, four legs and a small tail. Its favourite habitats are edges of forests, gardens and parks. It is active during evenings and nights, resting between five in the morning and eight in the evening. Hedgehogs are rather solitary and territorial creatures, and will easily fight with each other if they meet up at night. Their life span is from six to ten years.

Their sight and hearing are rather good but their sense of smell is excellent. A hedgehog's nose is always wet and sniffing and snuffling. Even a worm hidden 3 cm under the ground will not be safe from a hedgehog. His appetite is huge. The hedgehog is especially welcomed by passionate gardeners. Hedgehog food includes worms, insects (bees and spiders), snakes and mice. In critical situations they will resort to eating berries. The hedgehog has great physical strength considering its size. It can crawl through very narrow places; it is a champion long distance walker considering its small size and can walk up 3 km per night. It is adept at running quite fast and it is also an accomplished swimmer, swimming through rivers and streams with ease.

When one thinks of hedgehogs, one thinks of Great Britain and Europe. But, although it is not commonly known, there are also hedgehogs in South Africa. They live in and around cities in the bush and less developed areas. If you live near a green belt or a golf course, you have probably walked past hedgehogs without knowing it. Unfortunately when these cute little creatures come into contact with some of the byproducts of our human existence such as pet dogs running loose in the fields, they usually come off second best. A dog will instinctively give chase and if a hedgehog is caught, it will

probably be mauled. Hedgehogs defend themselves by rolling up into a tight little ball of spikes. This presents a hostile and painful target to the dog. If the dog is large enough, however, the hedgehog's defense mechanism is useless. Usually they are killed outright but on occasion they manage to escape, often with severe wounds inflicted on them by the dog and little chance of surviving. On rare occasions the injured animal may be discovered and taken to a veterinary surgeon or an institute for veterinary care.

I happened to be visiting a friend of mine, Dr Leon Louw, one of the vets at the Pretoria Zoo. The Pretoria Zoo is a world-class facility and truly is one of the treasures of South Africa. The zoo is a vast and magnificent area and the displays have been built with the animals' welfare as a prime concern. Keeping the animals contented and healthy is the zoo's mission. The enclosures are built with sensitivity to the animals and with due consideration to their natural environment. The success of a zoo is measured by the reproductive success of its animals. By this and any other standard, the Pretoria Zoo is a great success.

During the time that I visited, the zoo had recently been successful in breeding lions. Their pride and joy was the pride of lions known as the white lions of Timbavati. These lions had a heritable genetic mutation that caused their coats to be a very light cream colour instead of the usual darker colour typical of African lions. We had been invited by Leon to view the offspring. Whilst we were there, a little hedgehog was brought in for attention. It had strayed too close to civilization and had been cornered and caught by a dog. The dog mauled

HEDGEHOGS DEFEND THEMSELVES BY ROLLING UP INTO A TIGHT LITTLE BALL OF SPIKES. THIS PRESENTS A HOSTILE AND PAINFUL TARGET TO THE DOG.

IT WAS EQUALLY HARD TO KNOW HOW TO EXAMINE THIS PRICKLY LITTLE CUSTOMER. HIS SPIKES WERE HARD AND WHEN WE TRIED TO UNRAVEL HIM, HE JUST CURLED UP TIGHTER.

the little creature but its defense must have been effective because although the dog bit the little animal it did not kill it. The dog's owner was kind enough to catch the little chap and bring it to the Pretoria Zoo where they have a small but busy wildlife rescue unit.

While we were talking to Leon, one of the reception staff of the zoo came over and told him about the new arrival. He asked us if we'd like to be there when he examined and treated the hedgehog. We went with him to the treatment rooms where we were presented with a tiny little ball of spikes. It was hard to believe that it was actually a living creature. It was equally hard to know how to examine this prickly little customer. His spikes were hard and when we tried to unravel him, he just curled up tighter. Although we referred to the little chap as him, it was in fact just a guess. The only way to examine the little animal and determine the extent of the problem was to inject it with a powerful sedative that would render it unconscious. We would also be able to tell what sex it was.

While Leon filled a syringe with an anaesthetic agent, I put on a set of heavy leather gloves to protect my hands against the formidable prickles. Luckily Leon had worked out the dose from past experience and without too much fuss the correct dose was injected into the hedgehog. It took about six minutes for the drug to act and in that time we placed the hedgehog on the surgery table and watched. And wonder of wonders, as it drifted off to sleep the little ball of spikes slowly uncurled itself and we were presented with the cutest little creature.

IT HAD TINY LITTLE PAWS AND A SHARP POINTED LITTLE NOSE WITH LONG HARD BRISTLES FOR WHISKERS.

Lying recumbent on its back was a small hedgehog, completely unwound. We saw immediately that it was a male. It looked like it had stepped out of a Beatrix Potter book. Uncurled, it was a dear little animal about fifteen centimetres long with a coat consisting of sharp hard spikes that were in fact modified hairs. It had tiny little paws and a sharp pointed little nose with long hard bristles for whiskers. If Mrs Tiggy-Winkle had a husband, he was Mr Tiggy-Winkle to the tee.

Once unwound, the hedgehog was easy to examine. We found some superficial wounds on its back where the dog had bitten it. There was also a deep laceration that needed suturing. Leon cleaned and disinfected the wound and removed some of the necrotic tissue surrounding it. It looked like the wound was inflicted a day or so ago. There was swelling and inflammation but the situation was altogether not too serious. After cleaning the area with disinfectant and cotton wool, out came the suture pack and instruments. It was not possible to shave the area around the wound, which we would normally do around a surgical site. This was due to the simple fact that our razor could not cut the spikes! We cleaned up the area as best as we could and then sutured the wound. A hedgehog's skin is surprisingly thick for such a tiny creature and it is lucky that the suture needles were sharp otherwise we would not have got through the skin. After placing a few sutures in the wound, Leon closed it up. He then applied antibiotic paste to the wound and injected a small amount of antibiotic. The little hedgehog was then hospitalised in a heated cage and allowed to wake up by himself.

Wildlife generally doesn't do too well in a hospital situation. They usually are very stressed by captivity and the ensuing confinement. For this reason the best option is to try and return captured animals to their natural environment as quickly as

1. It's hard to believe that this little ball of spikes is a living creature; 2. Leon Louw and I treating the little hedgehog; 3. Asleep and unrolled, he looked like he had escaped from a fairy tale;

possible. The zoo has a policy of treat and release wherever possible and so we decided that the hedgehog would be examined again in twenty-four hours time and, if there were no further problems, he would be returned to the wild. To lessen the stress for the animal we gently restrained him for the examination instead of giving him a full anaesthetic. On examination our hedgehog was found to be remarkably well considering his ordeal. He was then released back to the wilds and it is our fervent hope that he lives a long and peaceful life and makes many hedgehog babies. The zoo made sure that he was released in an area sparsely populated with humans and dogs so that his chance of survival in the wilds was maximised.

Hedgehogs are needed in the wilds, not only from an ecological point of view, but also because they are magical, mystical little creatures who really do live outside of fairy tales.

A NOOSE AROUND THE NECK

POACHING IS A problem that is endemic to game reserves and wilderness areas throughout the world. The people at the top of the heap in the poaching world are wealthy but their foot soldiers are poverty stricken and when they can earn a meal ticket by killing off game animals for their masters, they do so without a second thought for the poor innocent animals that succumb to their not so tender ministrations. Their methods are for the most part very cruel. They range from gin traps and landmines to blasting animals with AK 47 automatic rifles. The result is that the animal is destroyed in the most inhumane way possible and the parts of the animal for which it has been killed are taken away for sale. Elephants are killed for their tusks, rhinos for their horn and lions, leopards and cheetahs for their skin. Some poor animals are killed because they accidentally stumbled into a trap not meant for them

There is now also a thriving demand for what has become known as "bush meat". This is the flesh from all animals without regard for species, scarcity, herbivorous or carnivorous. If an animal can be killed and butchered and rendered acceptable for the pot, it is called bush meat. It is quite inconceivable that the most rare mountain gorillas, bordering on extinction and also known as man's closest relative, end up as bush meat.

The poacher's traps are indiscriminate. There are some methods, however, that really defy the imagination when it comes to cruelty. I believe that one of the worst methods is the wire noose used by some poachers. This simple device is made with wire freely obtainable from a hardware store. I have even seen wire coat hangers bent to form a wire noose trap. They are set in the bush and haphazardly snare animals. The suffering begins once the hapless animal is snared. The

poacher usually monitors his traps only once or twice a week. If the animal is caught in the trap, it may be held captive for three to five days before the poacher's return. In that time, it usually dies of thirst or hunger or the wounds as a result of its struggle before the poachers return to dispatch it. In the case of a predator, the animal may actually gnaw off its own leg. In many cases the animal caught in a snare may become easy prey for another predator. On very rare occasions, the snare breaks off, leaving an ever-tightening wire noose round the animal's neck or limb. If this does not kill the animal by choking, then the wire noose cuts deeply into the flesh and the animal will usually die due to infection. This may take days to weeks. The cost in suffering is enormous; the gain to poachers is minimal. Often the poacher will find only the broken body of his prey with the desired parts such as the skins damaged to the extent that they are useless. Or a broken trap with an escaped animal out in the bush with a noose around its neck. It will die somewhere in the bush and the poacher will go home empty handed

Combating the disease known as poaching must occur at many levels. One cannot just hunt the poachers. One has to also attack the markets they serve by making the objects that are manufactured from the poached animals undesirable. Making a legal supply of ivory available from large stockpiled supplies of tusks needs also to be considered. This may reduce the demand for ivory and offer only a temporary solution but it seems to me to be more acceptable than burning vast piles of tusks from animals whose lives have been sacrificed for the tusks that are being burned. In the case of rhino

ONE HAS TO ALSO ATTACK THE MARKETS THEY SERVE BY MAKING THE OBJECTS THAT ARE MANUFACTURED FROM THE POACHED ANIMALS UNDESIRABLE.

IF WE CAN REMOVE THE POACHING LORDS THEN THE FOOT SOLDIERS, THE ACTUAL POACHERS, WILL CEASE THEIR ACTIVITY.

horns, education to try and dispel the myths of the horns' magical and herbal properties may also lessen demand. A concerted effort to try and unmask and control the poaching masters must also occur. The task is multifaceted and vast and it is unlikely that it will be solved for a long time. All that can be done at present is to try and control poaching by implementing regular anti-poaching patrols by dedicated personnel wherever there is wildlife. The remaining tasks need political will to be effective. Without that we cannot get to the core of the problem. There is an old axiom: 'Cut off the head and the body will die.' If we can remove the poaching lords then the foot soldiers, the actual poachers, will cease their activity.

There is a game reserve just outside that wonderful bushveld town of Hoedspruit, the centre of the game industry in South Africa. The reserve's name is Mhlametsi, which is pronounced 'Umshlametsy'. On one of his patrols through the reserve, the head ranger, Guy Arkel, noticed that one of the lionesses had a wound round her neck. On closer examination with a pair of binoculars, he saw that the lioness had a poacher's noose round her neck, which had caused a vicious wound that circled right around her neck. This was clearly a job for the vet so Dr Peter Rogers was called in. The plan was to dart the lioness, remove the noose and clean and repair the wound.

On the designated day, Peter arrived at the reserve and carried out what they had planned. The lioness was anaesthetised, and the snare removed from around her neck. The wound was bad and it was impossible to do much surgically except to clean it up and debride it. This involved cutting away dead tissue and applying antibiotic ointments to the actual wound, as well as injecting antibiotics and anti-

inflammatory drugs into the sleeping lioness. Once this was done, she was allowed to wake up and Guy was told that she needed to be monitored in order to ensure that the wound healed properly.

Usually these wounds heal up uneventfully provided the noose is removed in time. But with this lioness the situation proved difficult. The rangers noticed over the next few months that when she drank water, the water seemed to be leaking out of her wound. They also noticed that when she ate, small pieces of food would fall out from a hole in her neck that did not seem to want to heal.

The vet was called in once again. After careful examination with binoculars, a diagnosis of an esophageal fistula was made. This is a specific condition where a hole develops between the food pipe and the skin. Whenever the lioness ate or drank and then swallowed, a small amount of food or water would leak through the hole. The lioness was observed for another few weeks because it was hoped that the fistula would close up on its own. However, after nearly a month of observation it was decided that the hole would not close up and surgery was the only option.

I must digress here for a moment to talk about two philosophies that exist within the wildlife world. There are those people who believe that nature must take its course and the animal must live or die without man's intervention. Then there are those of us who believe that the situation that animals find themselves in is already so artificial that intervention is a logical conclusion to the massive intervention already inflicted by man. There are very few natural wilderness areas. All the game reserves are artificial and migratory routes have been

AFTER NEARLY A MONTH OF OBSERVATION IT WAS DECIDED THAT THE HOLE WOULD NOT CLOSE UP AND SURGERY WAS THE ONLY OPTION.

I SEE NO REASON WHY A HUMAN SHOULD NOT MEND THE WOUND.

severed. Many small private game reserves have purchased their stock at great expense and it is in their financial interest to attend to sick animals properly. In the case of this lioness, it was poachers who caused the wound. If a human caused the wound (although some of us don't call poachers human), I see no reason why a human should not mend the wound. I have occasionally watched wildlife films that film injured or dying animals – sometimes recording an agonizing death over a period of weeks. One such film that I watched was particularly disturbing. A pride of lions hunted and killed a zebra. In the process a lioness was kicked and her jaw was broken. She was rendered incapable of hunting and was unable to drink. The film crew continued to film her and documented her death over a week. I fail to see the entertainment or educational value of this piece of footage. Why was a vet not called in to dispatch the animal in a merciful way?

In case you are still in any doubt, I strongly believe it is our duty to attend to an animal's injuries to the best of our ability and as quickly as possible. We have eroded their habitat and created artificial areas for them to live in and it is our duty to look after them in the best way we know. And if the best way involves surgical intervention then so be it. It is in fact the least we can do. To stand by and watch an animal die in the name of conservation is inhuman and contrary to the spirit in which we merrily enclose them in artificial areas with imposed borders. And now I have that off my chest we will get on with the story!

The esophageal fistula needed repair, which could only be done under general anesthesia. The lioness would be found, darted and undergo surgery to repair the problem. I flew in from Cape Town and, after a restful night in the tented camp at Kapama, we met Peter at the Mhlametsi Game Reserve early the next morning. Guy and his assistant game ranger met us at the lodge. They had instructed trackers to go into

the bush to try and locate the lioness early that morning. So far they had found the spoor but had not yet had sight of the lioness. We all climbed aboard the reserve's offroad vehicle and drove off into the bush to try and meet up with the trackers. We were in radio contact with them and they told us that they were on to the spoor.

The vehicle took us to within a few hundred metres of where the trackers were. We had to leave the vehicle and go the rest of the way on foot because the bush was too dense to drive through. We walked through the bush in single file, led by Guy with his rifle at the ready. I followed next and then came the rest of the small group. Within a few moments we were with the two trackers. Guy spoke to them and came back and told us that they were on to fresh spoor and they believed that the lioness was not far ahead. With a measure of fear, I followed Guy and the trackers. I kept on thinking that this was not exactly safe. This was dense bush and it was entirely possible that we would stumble across the lioness. We were in her territory and the element of danger was physically palpable. The trackers kept on bending down and looking at the ground and pointing. I tried to see what they were looking at but couldn't make out anything. I began to start doubting them. They could be leading us on a merry chase through the bush with no lions anywhere nearby. I actually started to relax as this thought took hold of me. Silly me.

We were in a small clearing with the trackers about ten metres ahead of me when all hell broke loose. The trackers had come across not one but three lionesses and they had cubs. Animals will usually run from man but a lioness with cubs will stand her ground. She will certainly attack if she feels threatened, which is exactly how the three females with their cubs felt when suddenly confronted by humans. They roared and snarled very loudly. It is impossible to do justice to the amount of noise they generated. There were waves of sound washing over us in deep base tones. The sound actually reverberated in our chests. I was terrified.

I KEPT ON THINKING THAT THIS WAS NOT EXACTLY SAFE.

IF WE STOOD STILL, THIS WOULD CONFUSE THEM AND THEY WOULD HESITATE TO ATTACK.

Guy had briefed us at the start of our hike through the bush. He had told us that if there was a problem and one of the lionesses charged us we were to remain absolutely motionless. They would only run after and attack a moving target. If we stood still, this would confuse them and they would hesitate to attack. Well, difficult as it was, I stood my ground whilst the animals charged the tracker. Unbelievably, he too stood his ground. Guy quietly cocked his rifle and held it at the ready. This did not overly reassure me. At best he would have enough time for one shot. There were three enraged lions and if they did attack us we were in deep trouble. I wished for the safety of my house in suburbia. What was I actually doing here? My heart was racing and I really feared for my life. I stood there petrified, shivering and sweating in fear.

The standoff must have lasted about three minutes. Witnessing the trackers standing completely still with a furiously snarling pride of female lionesses mock charging them to within three metres of where they stood was the bravest thing I have ever seen. I have no idea what steel ran through these men's veins but I was highly impressed by their bravery. Then, as suddenly as it started, it ended. The lionesses melted back into the bush and their young followed. After the noise of their attack, the silence was deafening.

After what seemed like an eternity, the trackers started to move cautiously again and gingerly backed away from where the lions were. Once we were sure that they had in fact gone, we all relaxed and the trackers started to laugh with the release of tension. We were all very shaky and Guy decided that we should head back to the safety of the game drive vehicles. Walking around here was not for the faint hearted and right now my heart felt very faint!

Once back at the vehicle, we assessed the situation. It was felt that the lionesses had been very spooked and to try and work with them again today would not be a good idea. We

had scheduled a few days in the bush to try and help the lioness so we felt that we could wait until the next day in order to dart her and operate on her.

After some thought during the course of the morning, Guy decided to try an alternative approach. We had tried to track the lion and this had proved unsuccessful. It was time to try and bait the lioness into coming to us. The bait however had to be obtained.

Guy had seen a wildebeest in the bush that was sick and very thin. He noticed that its one leg was badly injured and its chances of survival were very small. He felt that it would be humane to dispatch it quickly with a rifle. This would be the bait. Once this was done, the carcass was brought to a tree in an area inhabited by the lioness we wanted. The carcass was gutted and then strung up in a tree using steel cables. The gutted carcass emitted a smell that was guaranteed to attract all predators in the area. The dead wildebeest was strung up to a height of about three metres. This was done very securely because we wanted the lioness to feed off the carcass at the site we chose. Guy told me that it was possible for an adult lion to pull the carcass down from the tree if it was not properly secured. The lion would then drag the carcass through the bush and take it far away before feeding. The only way to prevent this was to tie the carcass up very well using steel cables. It is quite an awesome sight to see an adult male lion weighing about three hundred kilograms dragging the carcass of an animal that weighs two hundred kilograms through the bush for a number of kilometres. Their strength is truly immense.

By the time we had finished setting the bait for the lioness it was mid afternoon. We were very hot and sweaty and had really been very frightened by the charge. The after effects of

IT WAS POSSIBLE FOR AN ADULT LION TO PULL THE CARCASS DOWN FROM THE TREE IF IT WAS NOT PROPERLY SECURED.

WE HAD DONE ALL WE COULD AND IT WAS NOW TIME FOR A STRATEGIC WITHDRAWAL.

the adrenalin release had made us tired and we decided to go back to our tents to rest for the afternoon. We left the baited tree with a tracker sitting safely in a game vehicle. He would remain in radio contact with Guy who would in turn call us if the lioness started feeding. We had done all we could and it was now time for a strategic withdrawal.

Back at the camp we made a fire and boiled some water for coffee and added condensed milk to our brew. This is a very evocative taste for me. It reminds me of my early game reserve days when I was taken there by my parents. It also reminds me of meals on trains traveling through the Karoo. Besides being delicious, it is always a comforting taste and was just the thing to drink after the excitement and fear of the morning. We took the opportunity to rest and clean up and lay in the shade of our tents for most of the afternoon. We emerged late in the afternoon and started to discuss dinner. We had booked to go to the railway restaurant that is situated at the old Hoedspruit railway station and were looking forward to a relaxing evening.

Dusk had just fallen at about six o clock that evening when we got a call from Guy. He told us that the tracker who was observing the carcass had called in to say that lions were close by and that there was every possibility that our injured lioness would approach the carcass and start to feed. He had called Peter Rogers who said that he would be right over and that operating at night was in fact quite a good idea. The game vehicles have bright spot lights that are used to view game at night. These make excellent theatre lights. Night time surgery has many advantages. It was autumn and the nights were cool but not too cold. Once the surgery was finished, we could place the lioness in a recovery crate for the night and let her out the next morning. This would safeguard her during the recovery period. Altogether it was a good solution.

Our supper would have to wait. We dressed quickly and drove back to Mhlametsi in the hope of finding our lioness. We met Guy at the lodge once again and were transferred to the game vehicle for the drive to the bait tree. We arrived there after dark and switched off the engine and waited. We could clearly hear lions communicating with each other in their low throaty growls and grunts. They were close to the carcass. We knew that they could smell the carcass because so could we. We had spotlights that were powered by the car battery. These powerful lights are essential tools for game spotting and we would also use them to illuminate the surgery area should we manage to dart the lioness. However, working at night had its drawbacks because a darted lioness could take fright and run and then we would have a problem finding her. But Peter was confident that once she was feeding solidly, the dart would not disturb her. He had done this before and we were relying on him for advice.

We sat for an hour or so and then a large male lion emerged from the bush and went up to the bait and sniffed. He then stood on his hind legs and attempted to wrestle the carcass to the ground in order to feed. The fact that the bait was dangling from the tree slowed him down somewhat and he was only able to obtain a small piece of meat. We did not want him to feed too long because the lioness would not approach the carcass whilst the male was there. There is a hierarchy within lions. Males feed first and only when they have finished will the females approach the kill. We did not however want to frighten him off as this could also frighten off our lioness who we were sure was watching. It was quite a delicately balanced equation.

WE SAT FOR AN HOUR OR SO
AND THEN A LARGE MALE LION EMERGED
FROM THE BUSH AND WENT UP TO THE
BAIT AND SNIFFED.

WE WAITED AND WATCHED AND OUR HUNGER PANGS MADE OUR STOMACHS GROWL ALMOST AS LOUDLY AS THE LIONS DID.

After allowing him to feed for a quarter of an hour, we started the engine and the sound must have startled the lion a little because he stood up and walked off nonchalantly. We were pleased that he had left and also satisfied that he was not too frightened. We were sure that we had not startled the female away if she was there.

Unfortunately for the next hour or so nothing further happened. We waited and watched and our hunger pangs made our stomachs growl almost as loudly as the lions did. Then, the real lion sounds started to fade. They were walking away and probably would not feed that night. Guy and Peter discussed the chances of success that night and between the two of them it was decided that we should stand down for the night. We returned to the lodge and then drove to the restaurant and had a very welcome belated supper.

It had been quite a day. Tracking lion through the bush, being charged by angry lions and then a night adventure watching a large male lion feeding. But the most important reason for my visit was still missing – our injured female who needed her surgery.

The next morning we awoke early and refreshed. We called Guy to ask him if the lioness had been found. Guy told us that the trackers had gone out before dawn to try and locate her. They had found the spoor but were worried because the lioness was on the move and seemed to be heading for the game fence that separates reserves from each other. The direction they were heading was east. If they managed to get over the fence they would be in the Kruger Park. The movement was unusual. The lioness usually hunted and rested near a water hole close to the lodge. She did not usually walk

extended distances. Guy felt that the incident with the cubs and the trackers and the pride charging us must have upset them and they were now moving to find safer territory.

A game fence has many different designs and many different functions. It can be used for a whole range of purposes, from keeping jackals out of a sheep enclosure, to keeping elephants in a private game reserve. It is not however all that good at keeping lions in one place. Like their domestic counterparts, the lion can jump a fence many times its height with relative ease. They can also dig efficiently and can easily dig under a fence. Some fences have a concrete foundation but not the one surrounding Mhlametsi. The lioness was heading for the border with intent. Guy was really worried and had asked the assistant game ranger to go and try to head off the lioness if it looked like she was trying to leave the reserve. I was not sure just how effective this would be. If the animals wanted to leave, no amount of shouting and trying to head them off would help. They would simply find a time when they were undisturbed and jump the fence. If they were sufficiently frightened, they would even abandon their young in order to secure their own future. If the adults survived, they would be able to breed again. The cubs were dispensable if the species survival was threatened.

Guy spent a worried day in search of the animals. Their spoor were seen and sometimes it was determined that they were really close to the trackers. Throughout the day they managed to remain steadfastly out of sight. At dusk, the tired trackers returned and a concerned Guy had a very restless night. We had set aside five days to try and help with this case and were prepared to stay in the bush until the situation resolved itself one way or another. We hoped that we would still be able to complete the surgery and help the lioness. But it wasn't to be – we never did see that lioness again.

The trackers found the place where they went over and under the fence. The adults must have dug a small channel for

THE LIONESS WAS HEADING FOR THE BORDER WITH INTENT.

the cubs to get through and then they must have jumped the fence themselves. They were headed east for the vast expanse of the Kruger Park and what they perceived to be safety.

There is a fact about the Kruger that needs to be mentioned here. If one combines all the areas in the park that are accessible to man, man has access to less than five percent of the landmass of the park. This consists of all the rest camps and a perimeter one hundred metres around the outside of the camps, plus all the paths and roads and fire breaks as well as a border ten metres wide on either side of the roads. Animals have over ninety five percent of the park in which to roam about undisturbed. The lioness and her pride could literally vanish into thin air if they reached the park.

The trackers tried to track the lioness across the adjacent reserve and found that she had once again jumped the eastern fence and was closer to the park than ever. From this point the search was abandoned. The trackers did not have permission to track animals across the reserve that the lions were now in. There was no choice other than to give up. Guy reported the incident to the various lodges and game rangers that lived in the area in the hope of being able to at least monitor their fate but to all intents and purposes, these lions were lost to Mhlametsi.

There were reports from the rangers at the Kruger Park that a small group of lions had arrived from a westerly direction but they were very skittish and ran away at any human approach. There was also a report that a ranger was able to get close enough to observe that one of the female adults had a substantial scar round her neck. These reports were anecdotal and unconfirmed but I like to think that they did in fact reach the relative safety and vastness of the park. Somehow this migration along routes directed by ancestral memory appeals to the romantic in me. We were unsuccessful in trying to help her surgically but maybe nature had her way and showed us that she can still take care of her own.

There is a natural cycle to things. The sun rises and sets every day. The moon goes through its cycles and many things in nature have their own rhythm. Modern man has made a concerted effort to influence and control many of these

1 & 2. After humanely shooting the Wildebeest, we hung the carcass from a tree using strong steel cables. We hoped this tasty meal would tempt our patient to show herself.

3. After being charged by the three lionesses, Guy and I broke the tension with a good laugh.

cycles and natural behavior patterns. In many cases man has succeeded outrageously in disrupting nature. However, there are times when man's influence and, dare I say bungling, has no effect on the outcome of events.

We tried our best to intervene. We set out to dart and fix our patient. She was caged in with game fences and artificial borders and boundaries but in the end her instinct was the strongest force and possibly ancestral memory. Our lioness disregarded our boundaries and fences and headed for safety. Against all odds she overcame every obstacle placed before her.

I am comfortable with the outcome. Some we win, some we lose, but in this case nature was the winner and I can live with that.

GULLIVER GETS HIS SIGHT BACK

OFTEN IN PRIVATE practice, a vet is asked to try and diagnose whether or not his patient can see. It is sometimes a very difficult question to answer. There are of course the obvious cases where there is clear visible damage to the surface of the eye, which is called the cornea. If the anterior chamber situated just behind the cornea is cloudy or damaged then a diagnosis is also quite easy. The next structure that we examine is the lens of the eye. This too can make the diagnosis simple. If there is opaque material in the lens then we diagnose cataracts. When these cataracts completely obstruct the view into the eye then the animal is unlikely to see out of that eye. There are a whole host of conditions that also render an animal blind but for the sake of this story we don't need a lesson in eyes. Suffice to say that if we can't see into the eye, then it is unlikely that a dog or cat or any other veterinary patient can see out of that eye.

Gulliver was a twelve-year-old Border Collie from East London, which is about one thousand two hundred kilometres from Cape Town. He had cataracts in both his lenses and his sight had been deteriorating over a period of time. The condition had deteriorated to the point that one could not see past the cataracts in his lenses. All you could see when you looked into his eyes were two shiny white discs obstructing the view into his eyes and his view of the world.

While cataract surgery is a routine specialist operation in humans, it is somewhat more challenging in animals. Humans sometimes have their cataracts removed under local anaesthetic. An ophthalmic surgeon performs this operation and there are a large number of them. The same procedure in the veterinary world is done under general anesthesia because our patients don't sit still when told to do so. In addition to

this, the number of ophthalmic specialists in South Africa may be less than the number of fingers on my hand. Gulliver's closest port of call for finding an ophthalmic surgeon was Cape Town.

Dr Gary had just recently completed his ophthalmic specialist training in Switzerland and had returned to South Africa to set up a specialist facility in Cape Town. The quality of his work was excellent and Gulliver's owners, in consultation with their own vet, had decided to send Gulliver to Dr Gary for evaluation and surgery if this was indicated.

Gulliver was flown to Cape Town and fetched from the airport by a family friend. He was then transported, none the worse for wear, to the specialist facility where we were able to meet him. I had been called by Dr Gary and informed of the case and with the owners' permission I felt that it would make a great story. I am very fortunate to have been able to witness so many highly unusual veterinary cases and this was definitely one of them.

Our first sight of Gulliver was sad. Here was a beautiful black and white elderly Border Collie with eyes that should have been clear and bright but were just a dull white. He had bilateral cataracts and could see nothing. His head seemed to weave from side to side as he tried to listen carefully to the noises in his surroundings in order to use his sense of hearing to make up for his lack of sight. The big question was, if the cataracts were removed would he be able to see again? If the cataracts are long standing, the visual mechanisms can deteriorate. Even once the cataracts have been removed, the optic nerves and retinas may not function. There is a whole battery of tests that have to be performed prior to cataract surgery in order to assess whether or not the patient will

GULLIVER WAS FLOWN TO CAPE TOWN AND FETCHED FROM THE AIRPORT BY A FAMILY FRIEND.

IF GULLIVER'S RETINA COULD NOT DETECT LIGHT THEN HE WOULD BE DECLARED PERMANENTLY BLIND AND SURGERY WOULD NOT BE PERFORMED.

see again post surgery. Plunging into surgery without careful consideration and evaluation is not an option. The tests are generally performed on the conscious animal twenty-four hours prior to surgery. This is what would be happening today.

As patiently as his namesake, Gulliver stood on the examining table whilst Dr Gary performed the various tests. He had been lightly sedated to ensure that he stood still and special anaesthetic drops had been applied to his eyes so that the procedures would be painless to him. There was a test to check the corneas integrity and internal health of the eye. This is a direct visual examination using a split beam ophthalmoscope. Dr Gary placed a strong light source on his own head, which looked like a miners' helmet, and used a hand-held lens to look into the eye. In the hands of a skilled operator this gives a wealth of information. There is also a test to check the internal pressure in the eye, which is called tonometry. If the internal pressure of the eye is raised, this is known as glaucoma. This condition is a common cause of blindness and if detected it should be aggressively treated. Another very important test is to check if the retinas are able to still detect light. This is done via electro retinography. A contact lens with a small electrode attached to it is placed on the cornea and a small pulse of blue light is sent through the cornea. The eye's response is measured and the ability of the retina to actually detect light can be measured. If Gulliver's retina could not detect light then he would be declared permanently blind and surgery would not be performed. There are also numerous blood tests. A very important one here is to measure the blood sugar of the patient. If it is raised

beyond a certain level then a diagnosis of diabetes mellitus is strongly indicated. This disease is also a cause of blindness. Diabetic patients have a predisposition to cataracts.

However, all the tests performed that day indicated that Gulliver would most likely be able to see once he had the operation. The blood test indicated that he was diabetic, which would have to be taken into account during surgery as diabetic patients tend to heal slower than non-diabetic ones. After all the tests were performed and evaluated, a decision was made to go ahead with the surgery the next day.

The surgery was scheduled for nine o clock the next morning. This was a refreshing difference to my normal crack of dawn routine for wildlife surgery. I rose at a respectable hour and made my way in a leisurely fashion by car to Dr Gary's hospital where Gulliver was waiting. He had been given a premedication injection that made him sleepy and increased the safety of the anaesthetic. He was placed on the prep room table and an intravenous catheter was inserted into the vein of his front leg. A drip was set up and he was then given his anaesthetic injection into the drip line. With a gentle sigh Gulliver slipped into unconsciousness and the procedure got under way. Once sleeping, he was carefully monitored and linked to various pieces of equipment that would display his vital signs. His heart and breathing were monitored and comforting regular beeping sounds came from these instruments. The skin around his eyes was draped off from the rest of his body and cleaned with a sterilizing fluid. Once prepped this way, he was rolled on the trolley into the operating theatre.

AFTER ALL THE TESTS WERE PERFORMED AND EVALUATED, A DECISION WAS MADE TO GO AHEAD WITH THE SURGERY THE NEXT DAY.

RIGHT THERE AND THEN A DECISION WAS MADE CARRY OUT A DIFFERENT PROCESS THAT INVOLVED TAKING THE ENTIRE LENS OUT THROUGH A LARGER INCISION.

Now this was no ordinary theatre but a specialised eye theatre. Most intraocular surgery is performed through a special operating microscope. This is a very expensive piece of equipment and a source of pride to Dr Gary. It has a set of binocular viewers for the surgeon as well as a set for an assistant. In addition, it has a television port and with the correct equipment, the entire surgery could be filmed through the TV port.

Gulliver was placed on the operating table on his right side with his left eye up to the surgeon. Both eyes were equally bad and both were going to be operated on that day. Dr Gary sat on his stool in front of the microscope and put his eyes to the viewer. I took up my position and placed my eyes onto the binocular viewer as well. The binocular viewer inverts the view. Up is down, left is right. It takes training and skill to get used to operating through the microscope.

The process that was going to be performed that day involved making a small incision into the eye through which a special instrument would be inserted. This instrument would then be inserted into a small incision in the lens and via high frequency vibrations and suction, the lens material would be sucked out, leaving the eye clear and hopefully with vision. This is called an intra-capsular lentectomy. The process is known as phacoemulsification and is the same technique used in human patients who are operated on while conscious and lightly sedated.

Dr Gary made his small incisions into both the eye and the lens but when he tried to perform the phacoemulsification it was found that the cataract was at a stage of hyper-maturity

that rendered this process of no use. Right there and then a decision was made carry out a different process that involved taking the entire lens out through a larger incision. The plan changed to an extra-capsular lentectomy

This is the mark of a good surgeon. Go in with your plan intact but for goodness sake, have a backup one just in case. When it is clear that your first plan will not work or if something happens that prevents you from carrying it out, then have a backup plan to carry on with. Versatility and flexibility are crucial qualities when it comes to surgery.

The incision into the eye was enlarged and the lens was then carefully freed from its attachments. Using a special instrument that suctioned onto the lens, it was gently removed through the enlarged surgical hole. The initial procedure would have taken about five minutes, but the procedure that we performed instead took nearly an hour by the time all the sutures were in place. The size of the incision that was first made was less then 5 millimetres. The size of the final incision to remove the intact lens was over one centimetre. The time-consuming part of the surgery is actually stitching the incision closed. When suturing up the cornea, the surgeon uses suture material that is significantly thinner than a fine human hair. The small needle that is attached to the suture material is only three millimetres in size and specially designed instruments are used, which facilitate the handling of these very small structures. Without the operating microscope and these instruments the surgery would be all but impossible.

Once the left eye had been operated on, Gulliver was turned over and the same procedure was performed on the right eye. The cataract in this eye was also at the stage that necessitated the entire lens being removed. Once again an hour was spent operating on this eye. What should have been

WHAT SHOULD HAVE BEEN A HALF AN HOUR OPERATION TURNED INTO A TWO-HOUR MARATHON.

ALL THE POST-OPERATIVE TESTS INDICATED THAT HE HAD REGAINED HIS SIGHT ALTHOUGH HOW MUCH OF IT, WE DID NOT KNOW.

a half an hour operation turned into a two-hour marathon.

At the end of the surgery, despite the process taking much longer than planned, Gulliver was stable and sleeping peacefully. He was removed from the table and handed over to the nurses for postoperative care. An exhausted Dr Gary finally lifted his head from the microscope. The surgery was a success – we now had to wait until Gulliver had recovered from the procedure and the post-operative swelling had gone down before we could find out if the surgery had been worth it. The big question now was, could Gulliver see?

I returned to the hospital three days later and went to the prep room to wait while the nurse fetched Gulliver. He was brought in to the room on a lead with a special plastic bonnet on his head to prevent him from scratching his eyes. There was a set of steps leading from the passage into the room and without hesitation Gulliver seemed to see them and climbed down them. This was in stark contrast to the first time I saw him where he was unable to negotiate the steps. We placed him on the table and very quietly I moved from in front of him to the periphery. His head followed me. I then took some cotton wool balls and gently threw them at him. He flinched before they hit him. There was no doubt about it – he could see. All the post-operative tests indicated that he had regained his sight although how much of it, we did not know. A day or two later, after having spent a week in hospital, Gulliver was discharged and flown home to his ecstatic owners in East London. The sutures that were placed in his corneas were made of a special material that would dissolve in due course so there was no need to remove them. The original referring vets were briefed and asked to monitor Gulliver during the recovery phase.

1. Doctor Gary and I performing a pre-op exam on Gulliver.

2. Dr Gary operating through the surgical microscope whilst I look on.

3. Gulliver now has eyes and can travel. I am kissing him goodbye.

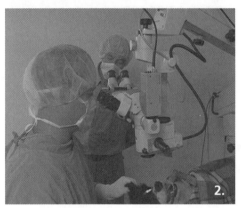

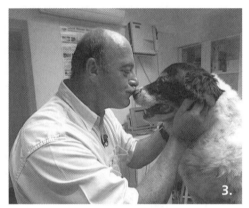

The story does have a happy ending. I received a picture about a month later of an elderly Border Collie. The camera caught the dog in mid air about half a metre off the ground on a beautiful beach. The dog had just caught a Frisbee. The caption written by the owners on the back of the photo was short and very sweet. It read as follows:

'Have eyes, can travel'.

ALL FOR A PIECE OF HORN

THE SO-CALLED APHRODISIAC properties of rhino horn are greatly exaggerated. I have had the opportunity to try some in a potion and I can give you my word that there were no fireworks and nor were there any phenomenal increases in any carnal behavior or lustful deeds!

Why, you may well ask, was a vet experimenting with the aphrodisiac qualities of rhino horn when his whole philosophy is conservation and preservation of both wildlife and domestic animals? Allow me to expand. As a student I did some work at the Pretoria Zoo, which had a magnificent resident rhino. He was about fourteen years of age and his horn was large, about one metre in length and a good thirty centimetres in diameter at its base. The 'horn' is actually made up of very densely matted hair and not bone as many people think.

The horn must have been itchy at its base for some reason and it appeared that it had been so for a very long time. There was a large steel gate at the entrance to the rhino's enclosure and the bars of the gate were just wide enough apart to allow the rhino to stick the full length of his horn through the bars. He would then rub his horn back and forth at the base in order to relieve himself of the itch. Unbeknown to the rhino, he also scraped powder from the base of his horn at the same time. The staff at the zoo were quick to take advantage of this opportunity and the powder was collected and sold to the 'muti' shop for quite a large sum of money. So in this situation there was no need to kill the rhino for his horn. Instead, the patient staff collected the small amounts that he yielded daily until there was enough to make a sale. This really was a continuously renewable source of rhino horn and the zoo authorities turned a blind eye to this source of revenue exploited by the African zoo assistants who worked with the rhino. The head of the zoo at that time was Dr Hymie Ebedes and he had a small supply of rhino horn that he kept locked in a cupboard in his office. Some of the students were offered rhino horn tea and I drank some out of curiosity. I can definitely vouch for its ineffectiveness!

At the time of visiting the zoo as students, we were in our final year of veterinary science. I was doing quite a lot of farrier work (trimming and shoeing horse's feet) and was somewhat of a (self-proclaimed) expert in foot and hoof care. The rhino in question was lame at that stage and had been walking around on a very sore foot for a few weeks. Dr Ebedes asked me if I was prepared to examine and treat the affected foot. Needless to say I jumped at the opportunity.

Now, you can't just saunter up to a two ton rhinoceros and ask it to allow you to examine its foot. That would be very foolish. As with all wild and game animals, the examination procedure takes place under general anaesthesia.

Dr Ebedes shot the rhino on its rump with a dart gun filled with a tranquiliser drug called M99. We then settled down on the outside of the perimeter wall to wait for the drug to take effect. This usually takes about six minutes. The anaesthetic process is, however, preceded by a brief period of excitable activity and a drug called ACP is usually administered together with the M99 to counteract this. Dr Ebedes had done this but it seemed as though this rhino required a bigger dose of ACP because instead of settling down quietly and going to sleep, it became agitated and for the one minute preceding full anaesthesia it suddenly broke into a stumbling run around its enclosure. We all looked on in horror as this enormous creature started to accelerate. Within the space of a few

SOME OF THE STUDENTS WERE OFFERED RHINO HORN TEA AND I DRANK SOME OUT OF CURIOSITY. I CAN DEFINITELY VOUCH FOR ITS INEFFECTIVENESS!

THE RHINO LAY UTTERLY STILL
ALONGSIDE ITS ONE METRE LONG HORN.

seconds it was in full charge towards the other side of its enclosure some fifty metres away. Now, when two tons of rhino collides with an immovable object such as a reinforced solid concrete wall, something has to give. Luckily the rhino was not able to accelerate to full speed because its enclosure was too small but it was still able to get up a reasonable head of steam. It struck the wall horn first. We all stood and looked on in shocked disbelief. The rhino literally crumpled up as it hit the wall. The noise of flesh colliding with concrete was a sickening sound. The rhino was snorting and squealing as it hit the wall and there was a loud ripping sound as its entire horn was torn off its head at the base of the horn. As I have said before, horn is actually densely matted hair so in effect a very large dense patch of hair was pulled out at the roots leaving a bleeding base. The rhino had been scalped.

I think that the horn possibly saved the rhino's life because the horn was able to absorb much of the shock of impact. I liken it to the serial collapsing of a car in an accident. This is a design feature of cars that enables the shock of the moment of impact to dissipate by panels serially collapsing.

For a few seconds after impact there was complete silence. The rhino lay utterly still alongside its one metre long horn. Then, out of the horrified silence a member of the zoo staff suddenly jumped over the fence into the rhino enclosure. He was dressed like all other cleaning and keeping staff in blue overalls and as a result of the speed in which the ensuing action was carried out, it would prove impossible to identify him. He had his wits about him however. He saw an exquisite opportunity and he literally grabbed it with both hands. He ran to the one metre long horn that lay in the dust and grabbed it. He ran like a man possessed and as soon as he got to the wall he threw the horn to looked like a waiting friend. This friend then ran with the horn for a short distance and then he too threw the horn to what looked like a waiting friend.

This went on for a very short while, possibly under a minute. The net result was that the horn must have changed hands about ten times in that minute and disappeared completely. We discovered later that it was spirited out of the zoo and was sold for a vast sum of money to the muti shop.

The scene we had just witnessed was so astonishing that it really bears dwelling on for a moment. It unfolded as though it had been rehearsed many times although how it could have been anticipated no one knew. There were about ten participants in the event. Person number one who jumped in and grabbed the horn initiated it. He then ran to the perimeter wall before passing it to person number two. Then in a series of passes that would have made a national rugby team proud, the horn simply disappeared. The entire process must have taken less than a minute.

The vets and students just stood and gaped in stunned amazement before shaking ourselves out of our stupor. Then we too were galvanised into action. Our action was not however directed at horn retrieval but rather at the safety and well being of our charge. We jumped down into the enclosure and ran to the recumbent rhino. Was it unconscious or was it dead from the dreadful impact?

To our immense relief it was found to be sleeping with only its large horn missing to remind us of the impact. The reinforced concrete wall was unscathed.

The rhino we were now examining had lost its horn and we were left with a wound that rather resembled a wound that would be left if one were scalped. There was a large raw wound about thirty centimetres in diameter where the horn used to be but it was a very superficial wound that would heal and eventually another horn would grow in its place.

WE DISCOVERED LATER THAT IT WAS SPIRITED OUT OF THE ZOO AND WAS SOLD FOR A VAST SUM OF MONEY TO THE MUTI SHOP.

THERE WAS A LARGE THORN THAT HAD BURROWED ITS WAY INTO THE ANIMAL'S FOOT AND FESTERED, CAUSING PAIN AND DISCOMFORT.

After all the excitement we almost forgot why we anaesthetised the rhino in the first place but once the situation returned to normal we were once again able to get down to the business of treating the rhino's injured foot.

The rhino was lying on its side and sleeping peacefully. All four limbs were protruding to the side and we were able to examine them with relative ease. I had brought along my tools for treating hooves and Dr Ebedes and I started to examine all four feet. We had decided to also trim and file the nails on each toe of each foot. I set about doing this whilst Dr Ebedes continued with the examination. Once I had finished trimming the toes he called me to examine the painful foot that was causing the lameness. It looked to me as though there was an abscess under the foot. There was an area about five centimetres in diameter that was discolored. I took a paring knife and started to try and open up the area in question. I only had to open up a short way before I encountered a pocket of pus that gushed out under pressure from the wound. We had identified the problem and it was an abscess. I dug a little deeper and discovered the cause of the abscess. There was a large thorn that had burrowed its way into the animal's foot and festered, causing pain and discomfort. Dr Ebedes believed that the pain may have been so intense that it cancelled out the sedating effect of the ACP, thus causing the animal to become over-excited and charge the wall.

Once all the pus had been drained and the thorn removed we flushed the wound out thoroughly and packed it with a special antiseptic powder. We then injected the rhino with antibiotics and Dr Ebedes gave the antidote to the anaesthetic intravenously. This drug is called M50 50.

The rhino woke up and stumbled to its feet. It stood a while and shook its head. Usually after the anaesthetic is reversed, animals stand up and act almost as though nothing has happened. This rhino, however, stumbled around for a few days after the treatment. We were not sure if this was due to the foot having been worked on or due to the massive collision between its head and the wall. But within a few days the rhino returned to normal – the stumbling cleared up and the foot healed.

This took place in 1984. The rhino lived on at the zoo until the year 2001 when I learned that it died at the ripe old age of about thirty-two. Its horn did grow back but it never again was a metre in length. It still scraped the base of its horn between the bars once there was enough horn to scrape. I would have thought that the loss of its first horn would have cured any itch but maybe it was just a bad habit that caused him to do this. Nevertheless, the continuous source of powdered rhino horn carried on Every now and again an infusion of rhino horn tea was offered to lucky visitor to the zoo. But I am still yet to meet someone who says that it makes one jot of difference to sexual performance.

THE RELUCTANT BULLDOG MOTHER

CHLOE WAS A pregnant bulldog and the odds seemed stacked against her. Firstly, she was pregnant and bulldogs can often experience difficulty in giving birth to their puppies. Motherhood does not come naturally to a bulldog – sometimes they lie on their newly born puppies and squash them and some bulldog mothers actually bite the puppies and kill them. Secondly, Chloe was a first time mother. This meant that her pelvis was not stretched from a previous litter, which could make the birthing process more difficult. Thirdly, ultrasound revealed that she only had four puppies inside her. A small litter meant that the puppies could be larger than usual – and may well get stuck in the birth canal. All this did not bode well for Chloe.

Dr Michael Gray, a practicing vet in Cape Town, decided in consultation with the owners that the best course of action was an elective caesarian section. This is a surgical procedure performed on pregnant animals -- and humans -- where the surgeon removes the infants from the mother via an incision into the abdomen and then the uterus. The infants are safely removed and then all is put back together with both mother and infants making a full recovery. Julius Caesar was supposedly born this way and the procedure now forever bears his name.

I had spoken to Michael who was a veterinary surgeon with an enviable reputation and had arranged to assist him with a caesarian when one happened to come his way. He called me and told me about Chloe and when she was due I drove to his practice prepared to assist him in performing the "caeser".

By the time I arrived at Michael's hospital, Chloe had pipped us at the post and was being given an ultrasound examination. We entered the ultrasound room to find Chloe

lying patiently on her back. I asked Dr Gray if she was sedated to which he replied no. I was surprised as she really was lying quite still and submitted without complaint to the procedure. Using the ultrasound probe on her pregnant belly must have been a soothing experience. We were able to view the puppies and counted four of them. Their hearts were beating regularly and at a rate that indicated that they were not stressed. Once we were sure that the litter was safe we moved Chloe into the induction room where we set up an intravenous drip line through which we administered her premedication. After this she settled down completely and when Dr Gray judged the time to be right, he induced general anaesthesia with a very safe drug known as Propofol. This drug has a milky appearance and is known colloquially as "milk of anaesthesia". Chloe closed her eyes and went uneventfully to sleep. There are times when things can go dramatically wrong with anaesthesia. Patients can go into cardiac or respiratory arrest and then all hell breaks loose as frantic resuscitation techniques are applied. These incidents however are rare and thankfully did not occur with Chloe. The nursing team then sprang into action. They had to shave Chloe's belly and scrub it for surgery and they also had to attach the various monitors that were needed to ensure that the procedure would be safe and successful for both mother and puppies.

Speed is of the essence when it comes to caesarians. The faster things happen, the sooner the puppies are out and the quicker the mother can wake up. For this reason there is a somewhat breathless period where people are working as fast as possible to ensure that the surgery begins in as short a time as possible.

WE WERE ABLE TO VIEW THE PUPPIES AND COUNTED FOUR OF THEM.

THE PATIENT WAS READY, THE INSTRUMENTS WERE READY AND MOST IMPORTANT OF ALL THE SURGEON WAS READY.

Once all the preparations were made and Chloe was ready for surgery she was transferred to the operating theatre. There another ritualised "dance" took place. This involved opening up surgical instruments that had been wrapped in drapes and sterilised beforehand. It also involved opening up sterile drapes and using them to cover Chloe completely leaving only the surgical site over her abdomen open. All this time the various pieces of monitoring equipment were emitting their beeps in time to her heart and breathing. These beeping sounds had their own rhythm and were comforting as long as they were within normal range. The monitoring machines were designed to emit an alarm if something went wrong. Thankfully Chloe beeped peacefully in the normal range and we had no cause for concern.

All the frantic preparations had now taken place. The patient was ready, the instruments were ready and most important of all the surgeon was ready. Dr Gray stood poised over Chloe, scalpel in hand. With a visible and audible intake of breath to steady his nerves, he placed the scalpel blade on her skin and boldly made his incision into her belly.

The technique of operating on a human abdomen very often begins in the same way. An incision is made along the midline of the animals belly through the skin. You then expose the inner layer of muscles and a strong sheet of tissue known as the linea alba or white line as it is translated from Latin. This is a tough fibrous sheet of tissue connecting the two sides of the abdomen together. In humans this would be the groove between the two sides of "the six pack" in a person with good abdominal muscle definition. The surgeon cuts through the linea alba and is then inside the abdomen. But from here on the surgeries differ dramatically depending on which organ one is primarily busy with. In Chloe's case it was the

uterus that we were after. The uterus is a small organ in the non-pregnant animal but when the patient is pregnant and the surgery is a caesarian, the uterus is massive. Chloe's uterus was very large indeed. Dr Gray exteriorised her uterus through the large abdominal incision prior to cutting into it. The length of the cut into the abdomen was about fifteen centimetres. You could actually see the puppies moving around inside the uterus once it had been exteriorized and was positioned on the abdominal surface. Once the entire organ was outside, a small pair of scissors was used to make an incision into it. This incision was then enlarged until it was large enough to grab a puppy from inside.

At this point it is worth dwelling on some salient points. Surgery done correctly can be remarkably blood free. You have to actually cut across a blood vessel before bleeding occurs. A midline incision into the correct site can miss most of the blood vessels there. The incision may only transect some very small superficial vessels so bleeding really is minimal. The cut through the linea alba is bloodless because it is a fascial strip joining two muscle bands that are all but bloodless. The uterus has superficial blood vessels but you can actually see them and thus avoid them. You make a small uterine incision and then cut along a bloodless area. In this way you can dissect right down to the puppies with very little hemorrhage. In the hands of a skilled surgeon, the surgical site is very often remarkably blood free.

The puppies are born in their fetal membranes. This is a set of "sacs" surrounding the puppies, keeping them bathed in fluids. All mammals have fetal membranes surrounding them in the uterus and are born inside this fetal membrane. Humans are notable exceptions to this rule and if they come out covered

THIS INCISION WAS THEN ENLARGED UNTIL IT WAS LARGE ENOUGH TO GRAB A PUPPY FROM INSIDE.

THEY WERE LARGE HEALTHY BULLDOG PUPPIES AND THEY WERE TRANSFERRED TO THE RESUSCITATION ROOM ONCE THE NURSE HAD RUBBED EACH ONE OF THEM.

in fetal membranes or a "caul" then they are thought to have psychic powers. These puppies were all born with their cauls around them but I doubt if they had psychic powers.

The fetal membranes have to be ruptured and the surgeon does this as he removes the puppy from the uterus. Each puppy has its own placenta and the fetal membranes are attached to the placenta via an umbilical cord. The surgeon cuts the umbilical cord and then passes the newly born puppy to the nurse waiting next to him. The nurse then has the task of rubbing the puppy vigorously to stimulate breathing and the expulsion of birthing fluids from the puppy's lungs. Sometimes the puppies need to be shaken to expel excess fluids from the lungs and airways. Normally a rough towel is used to rub the pups. This simulates the birthing process where the puppy is squeezed out of the birthing canal. The squeezing action is enough to expel fluids and stimulate breathing. Once this is done and the puppy is breathing and stable, it is placed on a warm blanket or heating pad and in a well-equipped hospital it would be placed in an incubator.

This process was performed four times over until all the puppies had been removed from Chloe. They were large healthy bulldog puppies and they were transferred to the resuscitation room once the nurse had rubbed each one of them. They were all breathing spontaneously and moving vigorously. The pups began to emit hungry squeaking sounds and were clearly impatient for their first feed. But they would still have to wait a while, as Chloe had not yet finished with her surgery. It was surprising just how vigorous they were. Many puppies taken out by caesarian section are sedated and very sleepy due to the drugs given to the mother having crossed the placental barrier. Sometimes they can be sleepy for hours but not so Chloe's pups.

After all the puppies had been removed, Dr Gray sutured the incision in her uterus. Sometimes the owners request sterilization as well as a caesarian. In that case, the uterus would be removed post caesarian. Chloe however was a valuable breeding dog and the owners definitely did not want her sterilised. Dr Gray used a special dissolving suture material to suture up her uterus. Once this was done, the task of suturing up her linea alba was tackled, then finally the skin was sutured together. The anaesthetic agent is a very short acting one. This meant that once Chloe was removed from the gas anaesthetic machine that kept her under anaesthesia she was likely to wake up swiftly. Dr Gray finished the surgery and then the gas anaesthetic was switched off. Even before Chloe was completely cleaned up she awoke. Clearly she was in some discomfort post surgery but this would be limited with the use of postoperative medication.

We needed to get her to her puppies as quickly as possible because they wanted to drink and the sooner Chloe had the chance to feed them the quicker the parental bond could be established. The puppies had a suckle reflex that remains in place for a few hours after they are born. If they do not get the opportunity to suckle within a six hour window of being born they lose the suckle reflex. To actually induce them to drink once this reflex fades is very difficult. It is imperative to get them to suckle soon after birth for a caesarian to be completely successful.

Chloe's owner was very brave and had decided to watch the entire procedure through the viewing window in the operating theatre. Once the procedure was finished, I had the chance of talking to him. He told me he was very nervous and had not seen anything like this before. I informed him that there were two boys and two girls and then led the proud dad into the resuscitation room to get his first glimpse and feel of the puppies.

WE NEEDED TO GET HER TO HER PUPPIES AS QUICKLY AS POSSIBLE.

CHLOE WAS THEN BROUGHT IN TO THE RESUSCITATION ROOM AND THE PUPPIES WERE PLACED NEXT TO HER ABDOMEN.

It is during moment like these that I feel very proud to be a vet and part of this little miracle. Jacques the owner stood beaming at the new additions to his family and his face said it all.

Chloe was then brought in to the resuscitation room and the puppies were placed next to her abdomen. Some milk was manually expressed from her mammary glands in order to allow the puppies to smell the milk and stimulate the sucking reflex. They were vigorous puppies indeed and with one small sniff of the milk they latched on to a nipple and started to suck for all they were worth. The let down reflex allowing milk to flow into the mammary glands is an involuntary one and soon these fat little newly born sausages had drunk their fill and were lying sleeping next to their clearly exhausted mother. Squeaking puppies are hungry ones; quiet puppies are contented ones. Chloe's pups were very quiet after their first feed.

Chloe had a lot of work ahead of her and so did her owner. He had to monitor the puppies and ensure that Chloe did not lie on them and squash them. He also had to ensure that they were safe from being bitten during those crucial first few days. We handed Chloe and her puppies back to her owner and they left for home and hard work. Dr Gray and his staff had quite some cleaning up to do. Surgery can be a messy business that requires a lot of cleaning up post op.

I wanted to keep in touch with the puppies and their mother to monitor how they fared in their first month of life. I made contact with the owner and he was happy for me to come and visit the puppies. I went to see them when they were about one month old. I arrived at his house and was saddened to find out that one of the puppies had to be put down due to a genetic abnormality. Its chest was far too narrow and as it got older the problem became worse to the

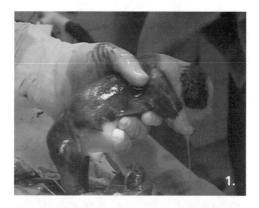

1. A puppy fresh out of the womb.

2. Four beautiful healthy puppies in the incubabor.

3. One month later, I visited the puppies. Moments like these make my job a joy.

point where the little creature was suffering badly. Dr Gray and Jacques, the owner, took the difficult decision and put the little chap to sleep.

I was ushered into a bedroom where the puppies were kept. I sat on the bed with them and realised that it was four weeks almost to the hour since they were born. So much had happened. They were now growing up and their eyes were wide open. They were mobile and had loads of skin to grow into. They suckled my fingers and squeaked and growled playfully at each other. These three little gorgeous bundles of fur and skin had their entire lives ahead of them and I knew that they would be bought by loving families and become invaluable members of those people's households. These thoughts echoed through my mind and I realised that moments such as these made my job the wonderful joy that it was.

CHEETAHS ON THE EDGE

CHEETAHS ARE ON the edge of extinction. Their numbers in the wild are almost at a level that is not sustainable. If the situation doesn't change dramatically, these magnificent animals, the fastest land mammal on the planet, will be no more. The cheetah's speed and power cannot save it from the challenges that it faces from hunting and poaching and being preyed upon by other predators, including man, in an ever-decreasing habitat. The current belief is that if it were not for the reservoir of captive breeding stock, the cheetah would be further along the road of extinction than it is already. Possibly the biggest threat to the cheetah and most other wild animals is their ever-eroding habitat. Too many farms have been established in wilderness areas with the consequence that the wild animals have had to move over for domestic ones. Fortunately this trend seems to have slowed down and has even been reversed in some areas. However, the damage has been done and the wilderness areas have been fractured to a certain extent by farms. Not only do the farms take up land that was occupied by wild animals but more importantly, the traditional migration routes of prey animals such as wildebeest have been compromised. Just one farm straddling a migration route can have an impact far beyond its physical size. We still have a lot of work to do in order to safeguard our children's heritage.

Kapama is a private game reserve in the Hoedspruit region and is situated on the western border of the Kruger Park. Amongst its many distinctions it is the home to "The Cheetah Project", the brainchild of Lente Roode. Her goal is to try to ensure that certain endangered species are at least well represented in captivity. It is her hope to have a breeding program so successful that its byproduct is the ability to

repopulate wild areas with cheetahs. She has been successful to the point that the project is able to sell surplus cheetahs to other game reserves, thus expanding the population. At this point in time, Kapama has the world's largest captive population of cheetah. This in itself is a tribute to the project's success. And it really is against the odds because cheetahs are very difficult to breed in captivity.

Professor Dave Meltzer is a world authority on cheetah breeding. He has been involved in the project's breeding program for many years and its success is in no small measure due to him. One of the challenges facing the breeding program is that the male cheetahs are all mostly sub-fertile. Their sperm count is very low, almost too low for a male cheetah to fertilise a female. In addition to this, many of the sperms have abnormalities, resulting in an inability to fertilise the ovum should they actually get the opportunity. This challenge requires regular monitoring of cheetah semen. This is done by anaesthetising the cheetah and then electro-ejaculating them. The semen is then harvested and examined microscopically in order to evaluate it for potential fertility.

I was lucky enough to follow this process through with Professor Meltzer while visiting Dr Rogers at the Cheetah Project. As I said before, Profs Meltzer is a world authority and to have seen him in action was a rare privilege. He was there to evaluate the semen of four cheetahs in order to see which one would make the most suitable sire for one or two of the females that were coming into season.

Dr Rogers' role was to go out and dart the cheetah and deliver them to Prof. Meltzer so that he could perform his procedures on the cheetahs and examine their sperm. Peter has done this many times and without much fuss he was able to deliver two sleeping cheetah within about half an hour.

POSSIBLY THE BIGGEST THREAT TO THE CHEETAH AND MOST OTHER WILD ANIMALS IS THEIR EVER-ERODING HABITAT.

THOUGHTS OF MEDIEVAL TORTURE CHAMBERS CROSSES ONES MIND AT THE MENTION OF THIS "SHOCKING" TECHNIQUE.

The reason that only two were brought in at a time is because the pick-up vehicle used for the transport only had place for two sleeping cheetahs. Each cheetah was darted and anaesthetised and placed in a transport crate and taken to the wildlife hospital at the Cheetah Project where Prof Meltzer was waiting. On arrival they were unloaded and brought inside and still sleeping peacefully when they were placed on the operating table.

Electro ejaculation sounds horrible. Thoughts of medieval torture chambers crosses ones mind at the mention of this "shocking" technique. It is not as bad as it sounds but to the uninitiated it looks dreadful. What it entails is inserting a special electric probe into the rectum of the sleeping animal and passing a very low voltage over the prostate area of the cheetah. When the voltage is applied, it stimulates the nerves of ejaculation and the cheetah ejaculates into a pre-warmed test tube. Sounds terrible? Well, it looks pretty bad too! However, the animals are sleeping and they don't feel a thing. We must also remember that the ultimate goal is to preserve the species so I think that this noble end justifies the means. I observed the process four times that day and after watching the cheetah very closely before, during and after the procedure, I am convinced that absolutely no harmful side effects were experienced.

Prof Meltzer approached the sleeping cheetah with the electro ejaculator probe in his gloved hands. This item really does look like it comes from a medieval torture chamber. It's about thirty centimetres long and about five centimetres thick with a copper strip on the end. The strip has wires running from it to a voltage generator, which is operated by cranking a handle to produce the low voltage needed. The voltage needed

to stimulate ejaculation is really low. If you held the probe in your hand while the voltage generator was cranked, all you would feel is a very mild tingling sensation in your fingers.

The probe was lubricated and slipped into the cheetah's rectum. It was inserted to a certain level so that the electrical impulses would stimulate the correct set of nerves in order to create an ejaculation. Once Prof Meltzer was satisfied that everything was in order he started to crank the handle on the generator.

Over the many times he has performed this procedure, he has found that a certain pattern of stimulation produces the best results. This involves turning the handle at a different speed for a set period of time and then repeating this pattern for a few moments until ejaculation occurs. I was asked to help the nurses hold the sleeping animal's legs. We all took up our positions round the sleeping animals. I held onto my designated leg with a firm grip. One of the nurses was charged with holding the tip of the cheetah's penis next to a test tube to collect the semen that was produced.

Prof Meltzer cranked the handle and what happened next nearly knocked me off my feet. The violence of the contraction that occurred in the leg I was holding was amazing. I was literally whipped off my feet but immediately regained my footing and held on with grim determination as the sleeping animal thrashed and writhed. Don't forget that the muscles of these legs can propel this 45- kilogram animal at one hundred and twenty kilometres per hour. They have extremely strong legs and I found this out the hard way! As the legs kicked violently I hoped that this was an expression of orgasmic pleasure and not pain. But of course the animal was anaesthetized and therefore couldn't feel pleasure or pain. The kicking out of its legs was just a reflex as a result of the stimulation of nerves.

PROF MELTZER CRANKED THE HANDLE AND WHAT HAPPENED NEXT NEARLY KNOCKED ME OFF MY FEET.

THE SEMEN SPECIMEN IS THEN EVALUATED MICROSCOPICALLY.

Once the voltage had been generated and the semen sample had been collected, the probe was removed from the cheetah's rectum and the freshly harvested semen was handed to Prof. Meltzer for macroscopic and microscopic evaluation. This in itself is a science that requires a highly experienced eye.

Macroscopic evaluation means that one looks at the sample to evaluate the color and turbidity – that is, the "cloudiness", of the sample. Is there blood or any other contaminants such as urine present in the sample? The semen specimen is then evaluated microscopically.

The microscope used to evaluate semen is called a phase contrast microscope. This generates light filtered in such a way that one can actually examine the morphology of individual sperm cells. Sperm should have a distinct head, a neck structure and a tail. If there are abnormalities in the actual structure of a sperm cell then it will be unable to fertilise an ovum. The percentage of abnormal cells, as well as the concentration of sperm cells in an ejaculate, is very important. It is also important to evaluate the motility of the sperm by observing them swimming around under the microscope. Sperm should swim in a forward direction with intent. If their motility is impaired they will not be able to reach their targets.

The sperm from the first cheetah that we examined was hopeless. The concentration of sperm cells was very low – far too low for a fertile mating. The percentage of abnormal sperm cells was also much too high for fertilisation to be successful. And to top it all, instead of swimming in a straight line, the sperm were going round in circles. Prof. Meltzer concluded that this particular cheetah was infertile at that point in time. The diagnosis was made "at that point in time" because it could change. Factors affecting fertility are still not altogether understood. There are many possible reasons why the cheetah was infertile, including nutritional and stress factors. If some of the factors causing infertility change in the future, it is very likely that the cheetah will become fertile.

Prof Meltzer performed the same procedure on the next sleeping cheetah with very similar results – it was also infertile. The second cheetah had in fact produced an ejaculate with no sperm at all. Semen consists of seminal fluid from various glands such as the prostate and bulbourethral glands. This fluid forms the medium in which sperm cells can survive and swim. The second cheetah had seminal fluid but on microscopic examination, not one single sperm cell was found.

Whilst Prof Meltzer was performing the procedures on the first two sleeping cheetahs Peter went out to the enclosures and, true to form and without much fuss, delivered the next two cheetahs to Prof Meltzer and his not so tender ministrations.

Within about one hour, all four cheetahs had been electro-ejaculated and their semen evaluated. The results were disappointing to say the least. One animal had semen that was of sufficient quality to breed with but the other three were completely sub fertile at that stage. If the survival of the cheetah depended on these four animals, then the species was in deep trouble.

The results were unfortunately not all that unusual. Prof Meltzer told us that over the many years that he had been involved in the evaluation of cheetah semen, he found this was the general pattern. Only one in ten cheetahs had semen of a sufficient quality to ensure fertilisation. Because of this, the various breeding institutions throughout the world had adopted a 'reverse harem' setup. This provided for more than one male for each female in the breeding colony, which stacked the odds in favour of a fertile mating – if there is more than one male, it is hoped that one of them will be fertile at the time of mating. This is in direct contrast to nature. In the

THE SECOND CHEETAH HAD SEMINAL FLUID BUT ON MICROSCOPIC EXAMINATION, NOT ONE SINGLE SPERM CELL WAS FOUND.

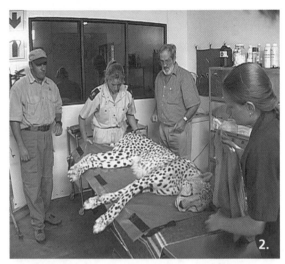

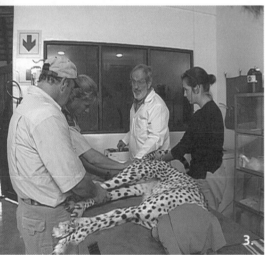

1. Dr Rogers about to dart a cheetah.

2. Sleeping cheetah on an operating table prior to electro-ejaculation.

3. Prof Meltzer cranking the hand of the electro-ejaculator as the assistants hold on tight.

4. Prof Meltzer examing semen microscopically.

THE BABY CHEETAHS WERE ABOUT THREE MONTHS OLD AND HAD ALL THE CUTENESS OF YOUNG ANIMALS.

natural environment, the males usually assemble a harem of females round them and in this way they successfully fertilise more than one female at a time, in this way maximising the breeding potential of their harem. The harem system, however, only works when there is a dominant fertile male.

At the Cheetah Project females that are in season are allowed to run in camps that have males in long enclosures next to them. In this way the females are stimulated by the presence of the males and the males are stimulated by the presence of the females. The staff observes the cheetah and the male that seems to be the most interested in the estrus female is allowed to try and mate with her. This has been moderately successful and most of the females have had litters using this method. They produce a litter of baby cheetah once a year on average. An average litter is two young.

Once the electro-ejaculation procedures with the males were over, we stood next to an enclosure containing a mother with her young. The baby cheetahs were about three months old and had all the cuteness of young animals. Their fur was soft and fluffy and they vocalized with little mewling sounds. They still suckled from their mother at this tender age and relied on their mother for protection and sustenance. These young cheetahs were a successful litter produced against all odds due to the dedication of outstanding vets such as Prof Meltzer and Dr Rogers.

It is at times like this that I swell with pride at having chosen to be a vet and it brings no small measure of satisfaction that I have been instrumental in some small way in trying to ensure that my children and possibly my grandchildren will have the opportunity to know these magnificent creatures.

THE
PUFFADDER
AND THE
MOTORBIKE

ALL CREATURES HAVE a right to life. The longer I live and work as a vet the more I have come to realize this. Of course, in a vet's professional career, euthanasia is often performed on request from the animal's owner. It is then up to the veterinarian to either perform this procedure or not. Most vets rationalize their decision to practice euthanasia by arguing that the animals that require euthanasia are old and infirm. If the animals are healthy then it must be remembered that the animal belongs to the owner who has the legal right to exercise this option. Another way of looking at this is to argue that some animals are in fact terminally ill and suffering in which case euthanasia is a better option. It is a very difficult situation when the animal is in fact completely healthy and the owner has decided to put his or her pet to sleep because it has become inconvenient to keep it. I have often passed this one up and refused to perform the procedure. On occasion I have also kept the animal at my practice and kept it until a suitable home has been found. Once I even agreed to euthanaze an animal because the owner insisted, but kept the animal without the owner knowing that I did not put it to sleep. I actually landed up adopting this little dog and kept her for nearly fifteen years. She became a treasured member of my household. I assume that if the owner had found out, I would have had his blessing.

But let's get back to my original statement that all creatures have a right to life; even the scaly poisonous ones that we instinctively want to kill. This brings me to an interesting story, which involves my friend Braam Malherbe again.

Braam was called out to collect a snake that had been driven over by a motor bike. The bike rider started his bike just before he spotted the snake in the road near his front wheel. He dropped the clutch, rode off in fright and the wheel went

over the snake's neck at an oblique angle. This resulted in shearing the skin over the neck area and actually lacerating it badly. He then turned back and, seeing what he had done, felt remorseful. In his fit of guilt he called Braam who was a friend of his. After receiving this call, Braam went out immediately with his capture gear and within a short while the injured snake was secured in a Hessian sack and lying next to Braam on the front seat of his Land Rover as he began his quest to save it.

The snake was identified as a puff adder. It was still young, about three quarters grown but certainly old enough to have an active set of poison glands. If bitten by this "teenager" one could expect to be in reasonable trouble.

Braam had not examined the snake very closely. He had captured it and then called me for help. As always, when it came to wildlife, I was available. We met at the practice and he came in with his dangerous cargo secured in the sack.

Puff adders are aggressive snakes but they are also quite lazy. They will lie in your way on the path and will not move until you have nearly stepped on them. If they take fright there is a good chance that they will bite you and move off slowly with their characteristically slow and shuffling slide. When a puff adder bites, it will actually chew on you a bit in order to activate its poison glands. The poison is then injected deep into your flesh via long hollow forward slanted fangs in the upper jaws. The bite is extremely painful and the poison is a necrotoxin. This means that it causes tissue necrosis and cell death. If bitten by a puffy, it is not a good idea to apply a tourniquet. This further exacerbates tissue death. The best thing you can do is to place the limb in iced water or wrap it in an ice pack. Only a trained professional should use Snake antivenin. In the wrong hands, it can cause death faster than the snakebite. The next thing to do is get to a doctor as soon as possible – preferably one who has experience in treating snakebite victims.

IF BITTEN BY THIS "TEENAGER" ONE COULD EXPECT TO BE IN REASONABLE TROUBLE.

THE SNAKE LUNGED AT HIM WITH INTENT TO DO GRIEVOUS BODILY HARM BUT BRAAM WAS READY FOR THIS AND HELD HIS CAPTURE TONGS AT THE READY.

The snake was tipped out of the bag and on to the floor. It was one angry snake by this time. It had been injured, captured, thrust into a bag and now tipped onto the floor. It was looking for something to vent its anger on and it focused on Braam. The snake lunged at him with intent to do grievous bodily harm but Braam was ready for this and held his capture tongs at the ready. He deftly sidestepped the attack and with a quick movement caught the snake's head in the tongs. He then moved the head from the tongs into his hand and kept the mouth closed between finger and thumb. The puff adder was both angry and scared and tried hard to bite but Braam held it tightly and within a few seconds it settled down and gave up the fight.

Now that it was restrained we could start our examination. We found a laceration on the side of its neck that was about ten centimetres long. The wound went right through the full thickness of the skin and needed to be stitched. It would not heal by itself and left alone, it would probably become infected and cause the snakes to die. We decided to anaesthetize the snake and suture the wound. However, this was easier said than done.

There is a combination of drugs that I often use for snakes, having ministered to quite a few of them. I use a combination of Ketamine and Domitor, which works well and keeps the animals safely asleep. The only minor problem is that if the animals are stressed prior to anaesthesia, the dose can vary a bit. A dose that would normally put an unstressed snake safely asleep may in fact not touch sides with a snake that has been stressed. Our current patient had been stressed so I upped the dose a bit. Braam restrained the head whilst I gave

the injection intramuscularly. We then put the snake back into the sack and allowed the drug to act. Usually snakes are asleep within six minutes.

After the prescribed time, we tipped out the snake only to find that it was not completely asleep. It was sedated and moved sluggishly but it was still awake enough to bite. We debated about administering another injectible dose but then opted to hold the snake's head under a flow of anaesthetic gas administered by a mask. Braam held the head in the mask whilst I administered the anaesthetic gas. Within a few moments the snake was sleeping and we were able to start the procedure.

I decided to use a dissolving suture material as removing the sutures would pose a problem in the future. I asked Braam to watch the snake and make sure that it was breathing while I started to clean the wound and disinfect it.

Making sure that a sleeping snake is alive is not as easy as it sounds. They breathe very slowly and their hearts are difficult to find and listen to with a stethoscope. Braam had his work cut out in monitoring the snake. While he was doing this, I proceeded to suture up the wound that I had just cleaned. I placed about twenty sutures in the skin of the neck. I was quite surprised at just how tough the skin was. I was nearly finished when Braam announced that he had not seen the snake breathe for a while now. I stopped my work and took a stethoscope and listened for the heart. It was still beating but very slowly. I tried to see if the snake was breathing but could not see any attempts at ventilation. We decided to switch off the anaesthetic gas and change to oxygen. Just how does one administer oxygen to a sleeping snake that is not breathing?

When a snake swallows its prey, they often swallow it whole. The prey is sometimes quite large and some snakes can voluntarily unhinge their upper and lower jaws to

MAKING SURE THAT A SLEEPING SNAKE IS ALIVE IS NOT AS EASY AS IT SOUNDS.

IT WOULD NOT DO TO ADMINISTER OXYGEN ONLY TO HAVE THE SNAKE WAKE UP AND BITE THE HAND THAT WAS SAVING IT.

facilitate swallowing a large prey. This process may take some time but the snake still needs to breathe. It does this by projecting its trachea or windpipe forwards so that the windpipe sticks out beyond the prey that is being swallowed. We decided to utilise this ability to protrude the windpipe. We took an endotracheal tube (a tube designed to be placed in the windpipe of sleeping patients), extruded the windpipe and slid the tube down. We took the end of the ET tube and attached it to the source of oxygen. I administered a drug called Doxapram, which is designed to stimulate respiration. Then, just to be safe, because we were dealing with a poisonous snake we took strong tape and taped the snake's mouth closed. It would not do to administer oxygen only to have the snake wake up and bite the hand that was saving it. Once this was all in place, we used a black rubber bag, called an AMBU bag, to ventilate the snake. Braam was charged with doing this while I finished placing the last two stitches in the neck.

I stood back and surveyed my handywork and was satisfied that the neck wound would heal. Braam continued to squeeze the bag gently. This had the effect of inflating the snake's lungs with oxygen. I listened to the heart and was relieved to hear that it was beating a bit faster. I asked Braam to stop ventilating the snake and we both observed the sleeping animal carefully. We were both relieved when after about thirty seconds the snake gave a slight shudder and started to breathe.

I finished off the procedure by injecting antibiotics and an anti-inflammatory and once we were happy that the snake was stable and breathing by itself, we removed the ET tube and untapped the mouth. Braam then placed the still-sleeping snake into the sack and went home. He has a herpetarium

at his home and is able to care for the many injured snakes that come his way. The snake was placed in the herpetarium, which is a large glass tank with a secure lid and was left there to recover.

The next day the snake was very still. Braam thought that it still was sleeping. He took his capture tongs and prodded the sleeping snake lightly. There was no movement. He tried to observe the snake carefully to see if it was still breathing. He could not detect any respiratory efforts and became worried. We had worked hard on this snake and it would be quite a blow if it had died overnight. Conditions in the herpetarium were very favourable and the sleeping snakes we had left there in the past had done well. Without a second thought for his safety he discarded the tongs and also the rule book for handling poisonous snakes and tried to grab the snake behind its neck.

Maybe he should have used the tongs or maybe he should have looked for a bit longer. Hind site is an exact science. He has had many years of experience with snakes but at that moment his only concern was whether the snake was alive or not and so he acted on instinct. He grabbed the snake and just as his hand was about to close behind its neck, it suddenly whipped round and bit him on the end of the thumb. It sunk its fangs into his thumb and gave a big chew, thereby injecting an excruciatingly painful amount of venom into his finger.

Braam has been bitten before and he has a lot of experience in dealing with snake bites. He does not panic, he acts deliberately and efficiently. The first thing was to ice the finger. He quickly went to the freezer, grabbed ice cubes and wrapped his hand in an ice pack made with a cloth. Then he called a doctor who had treated him before and knew what to do in the event of snakebite. Braam then drove himself down to the medical centre where the doctor worked. All of this took just fifteen minutes. In that time his thumb

IT SUDDENLY WHIPPED ROUND AND BIT HIM ON THE END OF THE THUMB.

had swollen up to the size of his fist and had turned very red. He was admitted quickly and given the correct treatment. The doctor placed him on an intravenous drip and gave him the snake antivenin while monitoring him carefully. He spent the night in hospital and was discharged the next day. It took about a week for the swelling to go down completely and today he is none the worse for his ordeal.

The snake was not dead; it was not even sleeping. It is difficult to explain why it did not respond to being prodded by the tongs. Suffice to say that it did not. But when it felt a hand around its neck it responded in the only way it knew how and that was to bite in self-defense.

Our snake spent a week recovering in the tank after which it was released into the wilds far from humans and other domestic pets. Hopefully it will grow up into an adult and be part of the circle of life.

This is not the first time that Braam has been bitten and it will not be the last. He is philosophical about these incidents. He just shrugs and says, "It goes with the territory".

Many people question why we went to so much trouble to save a snake. "Why not just chop its head off?" we have been asked. "Why not just euthanaze it?" Well, I believe that all living creatures have a right to life and if an injured animal happens to come my way, I do not question its right to live, I do the best I can to ensure that it does live. I have no doubt that if I was not meant to help, the puff adder would not have landed up in my care.

DELINQUENT ELEPHANT

TSHUKUDU IS A VERY special game reserve near Hoedspruit. It is owned by the Sussen family. The lodge is warm, cozy and user friendly. Here one can experience a game reserve steeped in the old traditions of hospitality. You don't need to wear designer bush clothing to fit in here but don't let that fool you, the food and accommodation are superb. Tshukudu offers a very unique experience that you don't often find in a game reserve – you can walk with the wild animals. They have hand reared wild animals that have become so used to humans that each day the game rangers conduct a walk through the bush where tourists are accompanied not only by the ranger but by a cheetah, a leopard, other herbivores and an elephant or two. But don't be fooled into thinking these animals are tame, they are not. Rather, they are used to the presence of humans and co-exist peacefully with them. The rangers are still armed with rifles and they know how to use them. They have never had to do so however and I hope they never will.

Tshukudu adopted two orphaned baby elephants, one male and one female, from the Kruger Park culling program about fourteen years ago. A few years ago, a wild elephant joined the small herd and the female became pregnant from this interloper who the owners called Slade, after a family acquaintance who ran off with someone else's wife. These elephants have been raised by the owner's family and are so used to humans from the regular contact they have with them that they form part of the game walks. However, beware: three tons of African elephant can still do a lot of damage so treading carefully is the maxim.

The problem with culling elephants, besides the obvious one of the tragedy involved in killing a magnificent beast, is that one is left with baby elephants. These vulnerable little

THE PROBLEM WITH CULLING ELEPHANTS, IS THAT ONE IS LEFT WITH BABY ELEPHANTS.

animals are then herded together and those that survive the terror of the cull are sold as infant animals to private reserves in the name of conservation. This is a very noble gesture, but the fall out over the years is great. Orphaned elephants raised on reserves don't have the discipline of the herd to guide them in their adolescence and so their behaviour often becomes delinquent, remarkably like a human that is raised in an environment where family discipline is not instituted. The result is that by the time the elephant reaches puberty, at between thirteen and fifteen years of age, we have a three-ton delinquent that behaves in an aberrant fashion. This deviant behaviour often leads to a conflict of interest between the reserve and the elephant.

The male orphan, named Temba, has, over the last few years developed some bad habits. He "plays" with the rhino on the reserve and actually gets quite "fruity" with them. He tries to mate with the rhino and generally picks on a female with a calf at foot. In his pursuit of amorous behavior he has unfortunately killed three rhino so far. A short sharp push with a tusk propelled by a three-ton body does a lot of damage. That tusk slices through a rhino like a hot knife through butter. He has also learned to use tools and uses logs wielded by his trunk and tusks to short circuit the electric fence surrounding the lodge.

Tuberculosis (TB) has become a major problem in the wild population and Tshukudu has embarked on a breeding program to try and breed lions that are free of TB. These lions are kept in a large fenced-off area and kept away from any game that may be infected. Temba has unfortunately also learned to use poles to break down the fences surrounding this enclosure.

The results of the elephant breaking into places that he should stay out of have been quite startling. Once he broke into the lodge pantry and ate over one hundred kilograms of

tinned pickles and glass jars of jam. He took the tins and glass jars, "cracked" them with his teeth and then just swallowed the contents, food, glass, tins and all. He was found with a severe colic, which is a major stomach upset. Now three tons of elephant with a sore tummy is not a pretty site to behold. You also cannot just walk up to him and ask him to open his mouth and take his medicine like a good boy. The approach to a jumbo with a sore tummy is quite different. My friend Peter Rogers spent a busy night treating an elephant with a very sore tummy. Step one is immobilisation with an anesthetic dart. Once asleep, the patient needs to be dripped intravenously with not one but sometimes fifty litres of fluids. Then the dose of opening medicine is so large that a platoon of soldiers would have their bowels opened by the volume of liquid paraffin administered. Once all this has been done, the elephant has to be woken up by using the antidote to the anaesthetic. This takes about two minutes to act. My advice to you now is to stand well clear, not only because the elephant is wild but because three tons of jumbo with opening medicine in his tummy, is really not nice to be near. This adds a new dimension to the phrase 'opening medicine'.

On another occasion the delinquent elephant freed the lions from their breeding enclosure and these freed lions, roaming at will around the camp gave the lodge staff and tourists quite a scare. Imagine coming out of your tent in the morning and being confronted by a large male lion looking for its breakfast.

The problem had deteriorated to the point that the elephant was becoming a daily nuisance and something had to be done. In consultation with Dr Rogers, it was decided to collar Temba with a radio transmitter. His whereabouts would then be known all the time and he could be monitored

ON ANOTHER OCCASION THE DELINQUENT ELEPHANT FREED THE LIONS FROM THEIR BREEDING ENCLOSURE.

HOPEFULLY HE COULD BE TRAINED OUT OF HIS BAD HABITS BY REPETITIVE NEGATIVE STIMULI TO HIS BAD BEHAVIOUR.

regularly. If he was found too close to the lodge or lion fences then evasive action could be taken. A gentle 'prodding' with the Land Rover would ensure that the elephants were herded away from the 'danger zone' into a safer part of the reserve. If he was detected near the rhino and he was behaving badly, he could be chased away. Hopefully, because elephant are such intelligent animals, he could be trained out of his bad habits by repetitive negative stimuli to his bad behaviour.

The collar is no ordinary piece of equipment. It is a special collar made from one-centimetre thick industrial belting with a radio transmitter and a special battery. A long-life battery is essential because changing it presents all sorts of problems. The battery powering the transmitter has a life of up to five years. The collar is strong enough to withstand the rigors of being worn by an adult elephant. It's an expensive piece of equipment and may cost many thousands of rands. The big problem is in fitting it. This can only be done on a sleeping elephant. Unfortunately elephants don't just stand still and present themselves for a "fitting".

There is a specialised drug called M99, which legally should only be used by a qualified person who is a "licensed act 101 practitioner". This means, when talking about game capture, a veterinarian. Doctors and pharmacists are also licensed act 101 practitioners but in the game world the vet is the logical and legal choice. The drug is extremely dangerous to humans and should be handled by trained individuals only and with extreme caution. The dose used to knock down an elephant can kill many hundreds of people. One small droplet onto the mucus membranes of your mouth or into your eye can cause death unless the antidote is administered. For this reason alone, it is advisable to use only persons legally licensed to handle this dangerous drug. There are of course many other reasons to use a qualified trained veterinarian in game capture cases.

We were lucky enough to be invited by Peter Rogers, a highly experienced game veterinarian and good friend of mine, to join him in fitting the collar. Peter has worked with wildlife for most of his professional career except for a short period after he had just qualified when he lived with my family for a few months and had a job with an animal hospital in Cape Town. This was for a short while only and since then he has been involved exclusively with wildlife.

We flew in to Hoedspruit and drove to the Tshukudu game reserve where we were met by the head game ranger, Ross. Our welcome was truly an African one where food, drink and hospitality were in abundance. We were shown to our luxury en-suite tents equipped with those wonderful fans circulating lazily from the ceiling. Once refreshed we made our way to the beautiful rustic lodge and we felt that we were transported back to the nineteenth century. The light inside the lodge was muted and we sank into large chairs of old, soft brown leather. It was just after lunch and we were served coffee in this beautiful setting. The afternoon was our own, as we would only start our work on capturing the elephant and applying the collar the next day in the cool of early morning.

Ross asked us if we wanted to go out on a game drive to examine our "patient" and become familiar with the surrounding terrain. We jumped at the chance of surveying the countryside and meeting the delinquent elephant. We climbed aboard the Land Rover and off we drove, in search of adventure and a troublesome member of the big five.

Our first encounter with Temba was really memorable. We drove down to the nearest waterhole and there in plain view for all to see, were about ten white rhino grazing. In the midst of this large gathering of rhino was Temba. He really was doing the strangest thing. He seemed to focus his attention on a female rhino with a calf at foot. His attentions were clearly

WE JUMPED AT THE CHANCE OF SURVEYING THE COUNTRYSIDE AND MEETING THE DELINQUENT ELEPHANT.

WE DROVE AROUND FOR A FEW HOURS THAT AFTERNOON AND EXPERIENCED SOME OF THE MANY WONDERS THAT TSHUKUDU HAD TO OFFER.

amorous and as much as she tried to butt him with her horn and fend off his unwelcome attention, she seemed to arouse him all the more. The noise of horn and tusk clashing in the quiet of the African bush was like a clash of drums. The rhino also vocalised and snorted her indignation. As much as the situation was intriguing it was also very dangerous for the rhino as Temba had already killed three of the rhino herd with his ardent attentions. Ross used the Land Rover to try and separate the courting couple. Once disturbed, the elephant ambled off into the distance and peace prevailed once more. This was a graphic demonstration of what the rangers would do in the future, once the elephant was collared. Once his whereabouts were easily ascertained, he could be monitored and if situations like we just witnessed arose, then the same action could be taken to break up the 'party'.

We drove around for a few hours that afternoon and experienced some of the many wonders that Tshukudu had to offer. We came across a cheetah that had just killed a small buck and was feeding on it. To my amazement, Ross stopped the Land Rover and climbed out. He then walked up to the cheetah and stroked her. He introduced her to us. This was Savannah, a hand reared cheetah that lived on the reserve. She was wild enough to hunt for her food and yet she allowed us to stroke her whilst she ate. While we petted her, she suddenly sat up straight and pricked her ears turning her attention to a specific direction. We became silent and tried to hear what had disturbed her. Only when we were perfectly still did we hear lions in the distance. Cheetahs sometimes fall prey to lions and Ross felt that it would be safer for Savannah to be taken back to the safety of the fenced area of the

lodge. He radioed some of his colleagues and they came out to attend to this. We then tried to find the lions we had just heard but it was getting darker and eventually we had to give up. They were deep in the bush and we could not access the area by vehicle. It was also not a good idea to try and find them on foot after dark so our lion finding expedition had to be abandoned for now.

The sun was now 'over the yardarm' so we returned to the lodge for sundowners. We first went to our tents to shower and clean some of the African dust from our bodies before 'washing' the same dust from our parched throats with the hunters' favorite tipple, gin and tonic. The evening meal is a story in itself. We were fed in true African hospitality. The amount and quality of the food was memorable and eating it in the open African air on the large patio of this wonderful lodge under a wide star-filled African sky will stay in my memory for a long time to come. After eating we retired, as we were due to start out early the next morning. Sleep came blissfully easily with the sounds of the African bush lulling us to sleep.

I wake early as a rule and it was before dawn that I started to stir. The African night sounds had not woken me from my sleep during the night but on wakening, they were still audible. The grunting of lions, the barking of jackals and many other sounds typical of the bush could be heard. Waking to these sounds is a wonderful experience. I lay still for a few moments just to soak up the sounds and the atmosphere. Day was breaking and the nocturnal animals that had been hunting and feeding at night would now start to move towards their lairs to rest during the hot day. We, however, started to prepare for work. It seemed as though the whole process was a changing of the guards.

SLEEP CAME BLISSFULLY EASILY WITH THE SOUNDS OF THE AFRICAN BUSH LULLING US TO SLEEP.

TODAY WE WERE GOING TO HUNT ONE OF THE BIG FIVE ON FOOT WITH ONLY A DART GUN.

I had a tense feeling in the pit of my stomach. Today we were going to hunt one of the big five on foot with only a dart gun. Admittedly we would have a ranger and rifle with us but that would only be used as a last resort. I never underestimated the danger of what we were doing.

If the elephant decided to charge us instead of running off into the bush, there is always a chance that the ranger would have to fire to frighten him away. If he still came towards us then the possibility of actually shooting him would be rapidly considered. Our safety was in the hands of Ross, the head game ranger.

We met at the lodge at four thirty am and had coffee and rusks. Peter Rogers arrived at about the same time and after a quick hello and coffee we climbed into the Land Rover and drove to where the elephant was last seen. A tracker had gone out before dawn to find the elephant and so armed with knowledge we were able to find Temba without too much trouble. By this time, the sun was up and it was light enough to see quite easily. We stopped the vehicle about two hundred meters from where the elephant was grazing peacefully and took our equipment out. Peter and I assembled the tranquilising dart and loaded it into his dart gun. The dart gun is shaped like a rifle and the dart is specially modified so that it can be used on elephants, which have very thick skin. The needle part of the dart is thick and long. The gun is loaded with a cap that fires the dart at a high velocity in order to penetrate the solid skin.

Ross, Peter and I set out on foot to track the elephant. We had to come from down wind or the elephant would possibly take fright and run away. He was not used to being disturbed this early and we were worried that he would suspect something. Elephants are remarkably savvy creatures and are acutely aware of their surroundings. We were sure that if he saw or smelt us that early he would know that something was up and would move off into the thick bush, which would make

our task much more difficult. We crept up on him quietly, using the bushes for cover and constantly making sure that the wind was in the right direction so as not to carry our scent towards him. The ground was very soft underfoot and our shoes were specially made for bush. The soft soles hardly made a sound in the thick dust of the ground. The situation was very tense. I could imagine how hunters of old must have felt when stalking an animal. Adrenalin pumped through my veins and my pulse was racing. We were just about within shooting range when he was suddenly disturbed and looked directly at us. We had been spotted and split seconds from then he would turn and bolt. Consummate professional that he is, Peter raised the dart gun to his shoulder and fired the dart into the elephant's hindquarters. Now whilst an elephant's rump is as big as a barn, when it is moving away from you at thirty miles and hour it is not that easy a target. Peter, however, is an excellent shot and his dart sped towards the elephant, hitting it in exactly the correct place and delivering its tranquilizing dose of M99. The impact of the dart is quite hard and the already startled elephant was given a further fright. He accelerated off into dense bush. It can take up to ten minutes for the drug to act and a lot of ground can be covered in that time so it is crucial to track the elephant. If he goes down in direct sunlight and lies there unattended for a long time he can die due to hyperthermia. If he goes down and lies in the wrong position on his chest he can suffocate. Finding him within a few minutes of the drug taking effect is vital.

The tracking team sped into action and the elephant was followed on foot. We too followed on foot albeit at a slower pace. We were in radio contact with the trackers and within about ten minutes we were guided both by radio and with shouts to where the elephant lay. During that time we were in dense African bush and once again I felt a strange unease. This

THE IMPACT OF THE DART IS QUITE HARD AND THE ALREADY STARTLED ELEPHANT WAS GIVEN A FURTHER FRIGHT.

I COULD NOT HELP NOTICING THE MARVELOUS NETWORK OF VERY LARGE VEINS COURSING THROUGH HIS EAR.

was after all wild bush and even though the animals were in a game reserve, they were wild. Walking round in their domain I had the distinct feeling that something was eyeing me and thinking 'breakfast'. Luckily we managed to hike towards where the trackers had found him without encountering any other animals. From a distance of about one hundred metres we could see that our elephant was lying in the shade and on his side. This could not have been better. We approached him rapidly and as I got closer I suddenly realised why this magnificent species was one of the big five. Not only big due to the danger of hunting him but big because that is what he was – very, very big. Three thousand kilograms of flesh and bone and muscle wrapped up in a thick gray crusty skin. Elephants are called pachyderms for a good reason. The word means thick skinned and that is just what they are.

Peter and I are veterinarians and our patients well being is paramount. Our professional knowledge takes over in situations like these and ensuring our patients safety comes first. We used a small stick of about fifteen centimeters to ensure that the tip of the trunk stayed open. Securing an open airway in an unconscious patient is very important. Then we flapped his ear over his eye to protect it from the sun. While I was doing this I could not help noticing the marvelous network of very large veins coursing through his ear. Some of these veins were as thick as my thumb. An elephant's ears are his bush air conditioners. He flaps them in the warm African air in order to cool himself down. All of the elephant's blood passes through his ears every few minutes and when he flaps them, he effectively cools the blood that is flowing through the ears at that time. The cooled blood then re-enters his body and in this way the elephant is able to cool himself down very efficiently. As our elephants lay unconscious in the

sun we used the same remarkable system to cool him down. We had a large jerry can filled with water and we doused his ears liberally whilst he lay there. This wetting effectively cooled the blood flowing through his ears and in this way we ensured that our sleeping patient did not overheat.

We applied some protective eye ointment to his eyes in order to protect them from drying out. Sleeping patients lose their blink reflex so the ointment was necessary to protect the eye from dust and flying insects.

It was my first close encounter with an unconscious elephant and once he was secured and we were satisfied that he was in no danger, I was able to step back and observe him. And all the wonder and magic of being so close to one of Africa's true giants just overwhelmed me. When you stand next to a sleeping elephant it is nearly as high as you are tall. Its abdomen is over one and a half metres in diameter at its highest point. The tusks on this particular elephant, whilst not enormous, were certainly long enough to do grievous bodily harm. Its skin is like the bark of a very old tree, hard and dry and crusted with mud. The patterns on the skin are like mud that has dried up in a pan that has not had water for a long time. I opened the sleeping giant's mouth and was able to examine his teeth, lips and tongue. Wonder of wonders, this animal, which eats thorn trees, bark and other really hard material, has a tongue as soft as velvet and teeth that have surfaces twice as large as a big man's hand. His lips are also very soft in comparison to the rest of his skin and I marveled at the fact that despite his diet of thorns sticks and other sharp objects, his mouth was so soft. His feet have nails that are as big as my hand and he has a sole on his foot that is wide and tough enough to carry him through the African bush for up to eighty years. African elephants can live a long time. There is a thorn

AND ALL THE WONDER AND MAGIC OF BEING SO CLOSE TO ONE OF AFRICA'S TRUE GIANTS JUST OVERWHELMED ME.

THE ELEPHANT'S NECK GIRTH WAS ABOUT THREE METRES.

tree in the bushveld called a "sekelbos" in Afrikaans. The thorn of the sekelbos is long and sharp and very dangerous. If one of these thorns penetrates an elephant's foot it can cause an abscess, which can render this powerful animal lame very vulnerable. We saw that one of these thorns had in fact penetrated one of his feet but had not yet caused an abscess. We removed the thorn and I am sure that had he been able to, our sleeping giant would have thanked us.

The dart that delivered the anaesthetic agent has a barb that enables one to screw it out of the tough hide. If not for this, it would be a very difficult task to remove it. To complicate matters, the tip of the dart still has some M99 in it; enough to affect a person very badly. I removed the dart and placed a cover over the tip to safeguard us from the dangers of the drug. There were some routine procedures that we performed on the sleeping elephant. Peter has a philosophy. Anaesthetizing game is not desirable, but when one does, it is a good opportunity to deworm the animals and examine them. If there are any wounds or other abnormalities then this may be the only chance in the entire life of the animal where treatment is an option. With this in mind, we injected a large dose of penicillin into him and gave him an elephant sized dose of injectible dewormer. We also treated some of the wounds on his skin topically. The final act after all this, was to do what we had set out to do – secure the collar round his neck.

I took the collar from the Land Rover and placed it round my neck. It came down to below my feet. That means that the elephant's neck girth was about three metres. Amazing. We slipped the collar under his neck and laboriously pulled it through to the other side. It was then secured end to end with a joining plate with four lockable bolts and nuts. This operation is not easy. One has to judge how tight the collar is on a recumbent animal. Too tight and it will be uncomfortable, too loose and it can slip off. If you are not careful it can twist,

resulting in the transmitter pressing into the elephants flesh. Over months this can cause serious wounds. With due regard for all this, we placed the collar on our elephant with just the right amount of tension and without a twist.

Once this last task was done and we were sure that all routine treatments were complete, we injected the antidote to the tranquilizer. This antidote is called M50/50 and works within about two minutes. The elephants usually wake up with no visible side effects from the drugging. The elephant's ear vein is used to inject the drug intravenously. I wish my small animal patients had such an easy vein to access. I was given the task of injecting the antidote and once this was done, we removed the stick from his trunk and flapped his ear back from over his eye. We then walked a respectable distance away from him and watched him wake up.

He flapped his ears and started to vocalize with deep rumbles that resonated in my chest. What an amazing sound that was to hear, truly a primordial sound of the African continent. He then rocked onto his chest and elevated himself onto his front feet whilst still lying on his hindquarters. Then majestically he rocked onto his hind legs and stood up. He appeared very relaxed and none the worse for his ordeal. Without so much as a "by your leave" he ambled off and disappeared into the bush as though nothing untoward had happened. And in truth, nothing had.

We switched on our radio telemetry unit and a strong beeping sound emitted from the receiver. When the directional aerial was pointed at the elephant the sound was strongest. If the aerial was pointed in the opposite direction the sound was weakest. This way, using the aerial, we were able to track the elephant and find his whereabouts. From that time on, he would be routinely monitored and if he strayed into an area that was off limits, he would be herded away. If he was detected near the rhino the same would apply. We hoped that

HE AMBLED OFF INTO THE BUSH AS THOUGH
NOTHING UNTOWARD HAD HAPPENED.

THE FOOTHILLS OF THE BLUE COLOURED DRAKENSBERG MOUNTAINS WERE VISIBLE IN THE DISTANCE. THEY ARE THE GATEWAY BETWEEN THE LOWVELD AND THE HIGHVELD.

this new ability to track him and know his whereabouts would assist in controlling his behavior. We did not know it just then, but the very next day our system would be put to the test.

We had been working since five am and it was now just after eight in the morning. All we had between us and starvation was a cup of coffee and a rusk. We had tracked an elephant, darted it, run through the bush, treated the elephant, secured his collar and we were now famished. The lodge and breakfast beckoned. We loaded our gear on to the Land Rover and drove back to the camp and a breakfast fit for hungry people who had done a full day's work within the space of three hours early in the morning. We were not disappointed by what we were given to eat. I was amazed at just how much food was on offer but what amazed me even more was how much I can eat whilst on location in the bush.

We still had the better part of the day left and I took the opportunity to walk round and explore the camp. There was a small kopje within safe walking distance from the lodge and I took a slow stroll there and climbed to the top. The vista was superb. The foothills of the blue coloured Drakensberg mountains were visible in the distance. They are the division between the lowveld and the highveld. The vastness of Africa was visible from this elevated vantage point. The colors of the bush blended together to form a picture that is etched in my memory. The greens and browns of the dusty landscape dotted with stunted bush and trees and the vastness of the blue African sky are unforgettable. I had arranged a game drive for late in the afternoon and inbetween my walk and the drive I took the opportunity to rest in my tent.

Our evening meal once again presented the kind of hospitality that one can only obtain in the bush. It was made all the more enjoyable by the hard work we had done during the day. Fed and watered, we made our way to our tents and slumber. I slept the sleep of the exhausted.

The next morning Ross the Game Ranger woke me after sunrise, a very unusual event for me as I am usually up before the birds start tweeting. He was very excited and told us that Temba had been detected near the electric fence just outside the far end of the lodge. This was an area that he had damaged previously and this particular piece of electric fence seemed to attract him. We were going to have the opportunity of testing our theory there and then. We used the tracking device to make sure that Temba was still where he was reported to be. We jumped in the vehicle and Ross drove us to the site indicated by the radio tracking device on Temba's collar. Sure enough, there were the elephants. The female, with her calf by her side, was standing next to the fence. Temba already had a log in his trunk and was using it to lean on the fence. Elephants are very intelligent beasts and Temba had learned to use tools to damage the fence. With a large log held between his tusks he was busily and systematically pushing the fence. Some electric strands were already broken and he was well on his way to gaining access to a prohibited area. Well, the moment of truth had arrived. Would we be able to scare off a three-ton elephant with a two-ton jeep? Don't forget that many a vehicle has been charged and flattened by an angry elephant and the occupants did not exactly benefit from the attention. Ross gunned the engine and we rolled slowly towards the elephant with all our nerves atwitter. We were about ten metres away from him when Ross blew the vehicles horn. With a sudden start the elephant tossed his tool

WITH A LARGE LOG HELD BETWEEN HIS TUSKS HE WAS BUSILY AND SYSTEMATICALLY PUSHING THE FENCE.

1. – 3. Temba was about the size of this baby elephant when he was adopted by Tshukudu.

4. Elephant being darted from a helicopter.

5. Temba as an adult interacting with the rhino.

6. You only appreciate the size of an African elephant at close range.

7. Ross and I tracking Temba with Telemetry.

aside and ran off into the dense bush. We all breathed a great sigh of relief; we had been successful and had survived the first episode of trying to re-educate Temba not to damage the fences. He had responded to the vehicle and we were able to herd him from the fence. There was still a long road to travel but our initial impression was that he was in fact trainable and with time and effort he would not damage fences. Only time would tell if we could divert his amorous attentions away from the rhino but at least the reserve now had a method of determining his whereabouts. And thankfully we knew now that he was not predisposed to charge.

I look back on that trip with fond memories. It was March when we were there, a beautiful time for game reserves in South Africa. The days were still hot but the nights became cool enough to sleep well. The bush was still green from summer rains but had started to thin out from grazing pressure so one could see game easily. I have subsequently been in contact with Ross and Peter and they tell me that Temba now moves away from the fence and leaves the rhino alone just at the sight of the jeep moving towards him when he is up to mischief. It seems as though the vehicle does not faze him when he is not doing something naughty. He seems to know when he is doing something he should not be doing and we all have hope that eventually he will leave the fixtures of the reserve alone and will learn not to bother the rhino.

The learning capacity of animals is only exceeded by the ingenuity of man. It took an elephant to learn how to break fences with a tool, it took a collar to help him learn not to do this and it has taken the skill and dedication of the staff of Tshukudu to ensure that there is a happy ending to this wonderful adventure.

PARROTS ARE MEMBERS of the Psittacine family. One of the peculiarities about many of the members of this family is that you cannot tell the difference between males and females from external examination. There are no visible sex organs and most of them show no difference in colouring between males and females. I say 'most' because there are some members of this family where the males have fancy colours and the females are drab. But in general, the above applies. Why, may you ask, is it important to know the difference between the two sexes? After all, the birds have been successful at breeding and sorting out the birds and the bees for many a long year.

There are now many bird breeders and this is a very lucrative industry. Some parrots sell for many thousands of rands. If a breeder wants to breed with his birds, he has to know which parrots are male and which are female, or he may land up putting two of the same sexed parrots in a breeding cage with poor results to say the least. There is also the possibility of the same sexed parrots fighting and causing quite severe injuries to one another.

Until recently, the only reliable way to tell the difference between sexes was put the parrot under a general anesthetic, make a small incision in the abdomen and insert an endoscope to view the sex organs. A skilled vet doing this work would then mark the birds with a permanent tattoo under the wing – left wing for one sex and right wing for the other sex. Once permanently marked, the breeder has no problem in placing the correct sexes together to ensure a successful mating. A potential new owner may also have a sex preference when purchasing a parrot so a correct diagnosis is important in order for the new owner to get the sex of bird he wants. I have even heard anecdotally that male birds sometimes prefer female owners and vice versa.

Tales of an African Vet

THE WORLD OF BIRDS HOUSES A COLLECTION OF BIRDS THAT CAN ONLY BE DESCRIBED AS WORLD CLASS.

The World of Birds is an amazing island of tranquility within the heart of a Cape Town suburb called Hout Bay. This bird haven is made up of a maze of paths leading from one aviary to the next. There are beautiful large trees that grow profusely along the paths, making a cool green canopy for most of the way. The World of Birds houses a collection of birds that can only be described as world class. They have both indigenous as well as exotic birds. All the aviaries are large with enough space for the birds to fly around in. The paths weave their way through the aviaries so that visitors may actually walk inside the large cages while the birds fly around your head.

Many of the birds were initially brought to the World of Birds with injuries. They are treated and rehabilitated but some have landed up with a permanent disability such as a non-functional wing or a leg that will not support them. They are perfectly healthy but their disability dictates that they must be permanently looked after. If you are ever in Cape Town, a visit to this place is a must. In addition to birds, they have a collection of very rare new world primates such as emperor and golden lion tamarind monkeys. They try to breed these rare little creatures and if it were not for the reservoir of monkeys in these and other international facilities then some of the species would be extinct. The wild populations of some of the species of monkey are simply too small to be naturally sustainable. If it was not for the captive population in existence today the species such as the Golden Lion tamarind monkey would be extinct.

My friend Rolf Nischk was the resident vet at the World of Birds at the time that this story took place. One of Rolf's tasks was to go to the bird hospital at the World of Birds once a month in order to sex parrots. The parrots may have

been donations from people who had to give them up for some reason, or they may have bought in new residents that need to be sexed in order to join the breeding programme.

It is interesting to note that a blood test has been developed of late that enables the sexes to be determined via blood parameters. There are some species of birds that have been bred in such a way that there is either a colour distinction or a specific colour mark (such as a small spot on the heads of a certain breed of chicken), which enables the lay person to separate males from females. I am sure that this non-invasive technique will surpass endoscopic sexing but for now, the endoscope remains the popular and reliable method.

I had liaised with Rolf previously and he promised me that the next time he went to the World of Birds, he would let me know. When the call came he told me the date and time of his next visit. I spoke to the owner of the World of Birds, a man named Walter Mangold, and he agreed that I could assist with the procedure. This remarkable man originated from Germany and came to Cape Town more than thirty years ago. He bought a piece of land far from any houses in Hout Bay at the time and his vision was to establish a haven for any birds that came his way, both domestic and exotic. Well, from little acorns grow big oak trees and today the World of Birds enjoys an international reputation that it justly deserves. The only problem is its location. When it was first built thirty years ago it was many kilometres away from any houses in Hout Bay. Due to urban spread however, it is now actually surrounded by houses and some of the neighbours occasionally complain about the cacophony of sound made by the birds. Still, I think I would rather have bird sounds than traffic sounds in my neighbourhood.

WHEN IT WAS FIRST BUILT THIRTY YEARS AGO IT WAS MANY KILOMETRES AWAY FROM ANY HOUSES IN HOUT BAY.

Tales of an African Vet

SHE OFFERED TO ALLOW ONE OF THE BEAUTIFUL GREEN AMAZON PARROTS TO SIT ON MY SHOULDER.

On the appointed day I arrived at the World of Birds and met Allan, the manager. Allan had been involved in zoo management for twenty-five years and was a recent employee of the World of Birds. Under his care, the place had become much more tourist friendly and the number of people who visited had increased.

While we were waiting for Rolph to arrive, I met with Jane, one of the parrot handlers. She offered to allow one of the beautiful Green Amazon Parrots to sit on my shoulder. With some trepidation I stood still and braced myself whilst Jane gently transferred the parrot from her shoulder to mine.

Now, while these parrots are used to their handlers, the experience of being on my shoulder was a new one to both the bird and me. I was somewhat nervous. These birds are huge. Their wingspan is well over a metre and their beaks are so powerful that they could bite a broomstick in half. My ear or nose would make a tasty snack and with a swift nip of their powerful beak this bird could easily have his snack if he wanted it. In addition to the threat of his beak, he seemed to want to exercise his wings and the bird (I think it was a 'he') decided that it was in fact time to exercise. He gripped my jacket tightly with his talons and spread his enormous wings and boy, did he fly. I actually thought he was going to lift off with both of us at one stage!

Once Rolf had arrived we walked to the hospital where the veterinary procedure would take place. There were four birds to sex. All four were new acquisitions and also young birds. They were conures and would be added to the breeding programme.

Rolf is very experienced and with little hesitation he put his gloved hand into the cage and quickly and efficiently trapped one of the birds. He brought it out of the cage and placed the

bird's head inside a mask attached to a gas anesthetic machine. This is a painless and safe way to induce anesthesia in birds. It takes about thirty seconds for the bird to sleep and they don't struggle at all. Once asleep, their heads are kept in the mask and the anesthetic gas is allowed to trickle at just the right rate to keep the bird stable and asleep. The bird is placed in right lateral recumbency, with its left side up. Micropore tape is used to tape the bird into position and keep it there. The feathers are plucked from a small area under the wing and behind the last rib in an area called the paralumbar fossa. Sterilising fluid is applied to the skin to disinfect the area. A sharp pointed pair of scissors is then used to puncture a small hole through the skin of the abdomen. This hole is about one millimetre in size. A sharp pointed trochar and canula is then pushed through the hole till it 'pops' into the abdomen. There is a specific 'feel' to this, one that is acquired through experience. Once this has happened, the pointed trochar is removed leaving the hollow canula, which is a rigid tube, leading into the abdomen. The rigid endoscope is then inserted into the canula and one can look into the body cavity of the bird. By visual inspection, an experienced operator can easily distinguish between testes in males and ovaries in females. Once determined, the endoscope is quickly removed and the area swabbed once again. The small incision closes by itself. A small amount of ink is used to tattoo the appropriate wing in order to identify what sex the bird is. The whole process takes about one minute, from first incision to removal of the endoscope. The bird is then placed back into the cage where it wakes up within a few minutes of the procedure being completed. I was amazed at just how rapid a procedure it was and just how unaffected the patients were post operatively. Within the prescribed time the birds

A SMALL AMOUNT OF INK IS USED TO TATTOO THE APPROPRIATE WING IN ORDER TO IDENTIFY WHAT SEX THE BIRD IS.

Tales of an African Vet

were up and about and displayed no ill effects at all. I know it is difficult to determine if this procedure was painful once the birds regained consciousness but on visual observation there was no difference between pre-operative and post-operative behavior. The birds were as mobile and vocal and hungry before the procedure as afterwards. Rolf assured me that in his experience, after having done thousands of birds, he has come to the conclusion that the birds don't seem to suffer from the procedure in any way.

Within the space of about fifteen minutes all the birds had been sexed and we landed up with two males and two females. I looked through the endoscope and only after some explanation and a picture of what each sex organ looked like, was I able to discern the difference between the sexes. It's easy in the hands of an experienced bird vet but to someone of a different background it was not nearly as simple as it looks. I guess that this is the sign of a smooth operator, one who takes a complicated procedure and makes it look easy and routine. That is exactly what Rolf did.

After cleaning up and packing his equipment away Rolf had finished for the day. Allan asked us if we wanted to tour the facility with him as our guide. Without any hesitation we jumped at the opportunity.

We went into the Emperor Tamarind monkey enclosure and were able to get really close to these gorgeous little creatures. They have very long white moustaches, which make them look very regal, and emperor-like. Once in their enclosure, we stood quite still. Allan had passed me some nuts and fruit and I gently and slowly extended my hand with a small morsel of food on it and waited. Within a few minutes these inquisitive little creatures were timidly reaching for the food on my hand and one bold little soul in fact climbed onto my shoulder and ran along my arm to get his share. One of the little animals was on a perch above my head and thought it would be amusing to anoint me, and that is exactly what he did. The little monkey urinated on my head. The small amount of warm fluid gave me quite a start because it was unexpected. The monkeys must have also thought it very

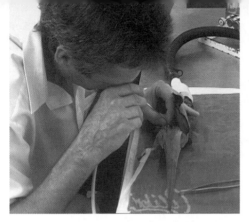

Left: *Rolph using an endoscope to look inside a parrot to determine its sex.* Right: *Me, slightly nervous, with a large coloured parrot on my shoulder.*

amusing because after this happened, they ran round the enclosure chattering and I could almost believe that they were laughing and pointing at me.

We left the enclosure and Allan showed us through other beautiful areas. We stood inside the aviary housing an entire flock of Red Ibises from Egypt. We were also given the opportunity to look at their very rare Golden Lion Tamarind breeding pair. They own one of the little creatures and an overseas zoo owns the other one. The little male and female were placed together in the hope that a successful mating would produce another of these very rare little creatures. The numbers worldwide are too small to sustain them in the wilds. The only Golden Lion Tamarinds left in the world are housed in captivity in institutions that are trying to breed them and increase the population. I felt privileged to be looking at such a rare little creature but also profoundly sad that the chance of their survival as a species was very small.

It seems to me that a common end with many an interlude is the sharing of refreshments and this time there was not an exception. After the tour Allan invited us to the amply stocked cafeteria just near the entrance. It was a chance to relax for a few moments and to take stock of our experiences. We shared a laugh over my getting anointed and felt that this had been altogether a great experience. The World of Bird's mission to save birds and other endangered little creatures is laudable and a visit to this special place is time well spent.

Tales of an African Vet

I FIRST MET Dr Fritz Huchzermeyer when I was a veterinary student. I found him to be a very interesting person and his skills were exceptional. He had spent five years on the Galapagos Islands studying at the Charles Darwin institute and was truly an internationally recognised expert. His particular set of skills was also very unusual. He was a world authority on, of all creatures, ostriches and crocodiles. He also knew more about tortoises than anyone else I have ever encountered. He has written definitive text books on ostriches and crocodiles and has published numerous articles on the creatures he has made a study of his whole life.

Crocodiles are currently the flavour of many wildlife television shows. Sadly Steve Irwin, the original "crocodile hunter", met an untimely end as fate would have it when he succumbed to the sting of a ray whilst filming on site at the Great Barrier Reef. However, he was better known for his escapades with crocodiles. I have a great fascination for these creatures and I therefore naturally gravitated towards Dr Huchzermeyer and called him to ask if I could accompany him on a clinical case where he would handle and treat a crocodile. I was keen to observe first hand how this was done and wanted to ask many questions about these creatures from a veterinary perspective. After long conversations with him, I discovered that in fact one does not actually treat adult crocodiles clinically. I will explain more about this strange anomaly later.

Crocodiles are farmed these days and very successfully I might add. Prior to being farmed, the Nile crocodile was on the CITES endangered wildlife list. There are numerous CITES lists. Animals that are most endangered and whose survival is seriously threatened are on the CITES 1 list. The lists are

DR HUCHZERMEYER'S MAIN FUNCTION THERE WAS TO MONITOR WHAT HE REFERRED TO AS HERD HEALTH.

numbered in increasing order. Animals on CITES 2 are less endangered than animals on CITES 1 and so on. The lists are management tools in order to help conserve endangered species. The Nile crocodile was on CITES 3 list at one stage but now it is off the list and their survival is ensured for the present. Their numbers in the wild had dwindled to the point where their survival as a species was seriously threatened. The farming enterprise however has been so successful that their numbers are now well within the range that ensures survival. Stocks of crocodiles on farms are large. There are some massive enterprises in Southern Africa and this is one of the few instances where commercial interests and wildlife interests have led to the survival of a species.

Dr Huchzermeyer is a consultant to numerous crocodile farms and told me that his main function there was to monitor what he referred to as herd health. This included the detection and prevention of disease, as opposed to treatment of sick individuals. He offered to take me along to two farms and show me what he did there. The main activity in managing the croc flock was to draw blood regularly from young crocodiles and monitor certain parameters that indicated that the animals were stressed. The whole idea here is to minimise stress and maximise growth and production.

We met at his smallholding on the eastern outskirts of Pretoria early one morning and drove some fifty kilometres to get to the first farm. We would be looking at and discussing adult crocodiles on this particular farm and would then travel to another farm nearby to handle smaller individuals where he would show us what the monitoring process entails.

The "farm" consists of two general areas. There are large barns where the young crocs are kept indoors in ponds. The conditions in these indoor paddocks are kept constant to

Tales of an African Vet

ensure that the young crocodiles of up to about one point five metres are raised in optimum conditions. The second general area is where the adult crocodiles were kept. This area is a very large man-made lake that must measure about two hundred metres in diameter. A brick wall roughly two metres high surrounds the entire lake. The lake is in the open air and surrounded by a concrete "shore". There are also islands in the lake. Round the perimeter of the lake, the "shoreline" slopes gently into the water. On the shoreline, against the perimeter wall, there are numerous pens with earth flooring. This is where the female crocodiles lay their eggs. Low walls separate the pens from each other, allowing an individual crocodile to lay her eggs in peace once inside her pen. The pens are also numbered to facilitate identification.

The females lay their eggs at night and then bury the eggs in the sand just under the surface of the pen. The laying pens are monitored daily and once eggs are laid they are removed from the pens and placed in the hatchery. Dr Huchzermeyer jokingly told us that the highest paid individual on the farm was the man who removed the eggs from the nests in the morning! In fact there were two men involved in this task, one with a stick to fend off the attention of any crocodile close by and the other to harvest the eggs. The crocodile left their nests during the day and retreated to the water so harvesting the eggs is not the extremely dangerous task we initially thought it was.

Whilst showing me round the farm, Dr Huchzermeyer shared some fascinating information with me.

The life span of a crocodile is very similar to the life span of a human. They live to between seventy and eighty years of age. They are small and relatively helpless at birth. They go

HE TOLD US THAT THE HIGHEST PAID INDIVIDUAL ON THE FARM WAS THE MAN WHO REMOVED THE EGGS FROM THE NESTS IN THE MORNING!

THEY SEEM TO LIVE IN FLOCKS, SIMILAR TO BIRDS.

through puberty between ten and thirteen years of age and they keep on growing in length until they reach the age of about eighteen or twenty. They are then regarded as adults. From here on they don't get longer, just fatter. Crocodiles become old and cranky from their mid forties, just like some humans! From about this age they start to lose their vigour and it is a slow downhill roll from this point until they die at seventy odd. They are in their sexual and breeding prime during their twenties and thirties. The similarity in the life stages of crocs and humans is almost laughable!

They make very good parents and unlike other reptiles they don't abandon their young but actually look after them and guard them during their infancy. The similarity to birds is notable. Once the young crocodiles reach a certain length they are chased away by the adults but this can take a few years before it happens. They seem to live in flocks, similar to birds. In fact, Dr Huchzermeyer repeated often that their behaviour is remarkably similar to bird behaviour. Birds are thought to be the modern descendants of the dinosaurs and crocodiles are thought to be the only remaining survivors from the dinosaur period.

Crocodiles have a number of ways of moving. They can swim in the water using their webbed feet and powerful tail to propel them. They slither on mud and sand using their legs to paddle their bodies forward. When they do this they leave the characteristic "slide" marks that identify that crocs have been around. They walk with their bodies elevated above the ground and they waddle onto sandy beaches in order to bask in the sun. This is their chosen gait for moving around on land when they are not in a hurry. Lastly, they can gallop. When hunting, they observe their prey from under water with just their eyes and nostrils sticking out of the water. Then, when they judge the time to be right, they give a sudden very powerful thrash of their tail and launch themselves at full

gallop towards their hapless prey at about forty kilometres an hour. This means that if the prey is within ten metres of the edge of the pond the croc will cover that distance in a second. This is not enough time for escape and their success rate at hunting for prey in this manner is very high. Tribal fishermen occasionally fall prey to a croc that launches itself in this manner. The poor human just does not have the time to move out of the way and if the croc is large enough then unfortunately it will be able to drag the person into the water and drown him or her. People are seldom found after such an attack. Crocodiles have lairs underwater in caves that are submerged and are supposed to store their prey there, allowing the flesh to rot before consuming the meat. What a dreadful way to meet your end.

Crocodiles breathe air through their nostrils but they are able to slow their heart and respiration rate down so dramatically that under certain circumstances they can remain under water for two hours without breathing. They can also compress the volume of air in their lungs so that this air acts as a diving chamber. When the chamber is expanded, the croc will rise to the surface and when compressed the croc will sink below the surface. This is a voluntary action and this is why they are able to rise or submerge silently with no movement of any visible part of their bodies.

In summer they feed once a week but in the cold of winter their metabolism slows down so dramatically that they actually don't need food for months on end. If they feed in winter, the food can rot in their intestines causing their death.

Crocs regulate their body temperatures by basking in the sun to warm themselves up. If they overheat they counteract this by "gaping". They lie with their mouths open and in this way get rid of excess heat. They will also obviously go into

UNDER CERTAIN CIRCUMSTANCES THEY CAN REMAIN UNDER WATER FOR TWO HOURS WITHOUT BREATHING.

THE POND WAS FILLED WITH WELL OVER TWO HUNDRED CROCODILES.

water if it gets too hot. In the cool of the morning crocs are sluggish and cannot move fast so they don't hunt early. They are most dangerous during the warm part of the day when their bodies have warmed up and they can move quickly.

As I mentioned previously, by the time the animals exhibit signs of disease, they are generally too sick to survive. There is also the practical problem of clinically examining and treating these large strong reptiles. The best form of care for these animals is to try and monitor the health of the entire "flock" of crocs and to ensure that they live in a stress-free, clean and healthy environment. In this way disease is prevented because it is difficult, if not impossible, to actually cure a sick crock.

Dr Huchzermeyer told us all these fascinating facts whilst we were standing on an island in the middle of the pond I described above. What I did not tell you was that the pond was filled with well over two hundred crocodiles, the smallest of which must have been three metres. They lazed on the shore, they swam silently round in the water, and they nested in their enclosures. In fact, wherever you looked there were crocodiles. The island we stood on was linked to the outside of the enclosure by a gantry over the water and a croc proof fence surrounded our island. This was the service area that was used to clean and maintain the filter equipment for the pond.

Whilst standing and talking to the croc doc, my foot protruded over the walkway and stuck out about fifteen centimetres over the water. Dr Huchzermeyer suddenly noticed this and quickly pulled me away from the edge. Just as he did this, a large croc emerged beneath me. It had clearly seen my foot sticking out and had come to investigate. Dr H told me that if it had launched itself at me I would not have had time to pull my leg away and we may have had a serious problem. I actually got quite a fright and needless to say kept well clear of the edge after that.

Once we had seen the adult animals and he had given us all these fascinating facts we were taken to the second farm. There we had the chance to examine and handle the young animals and we were also taken into a hatchery to look at eggs and hatchlings. But the climax of this visit was feeding the crocs – more about that later. The second farm was a twenty-minute drive and if I thought that the adults crocs were interesting, they paled into insignificance when compared with the young crocodiles.

One must not forget that this is a farming enterprise. The farm produces a product, namely crocodile skins and crocodile meat. This means that somewhere along the line the animals are slaughtered and processed into a product that can be sold. Individuals have a commercial value so their production must be optimised. This means that they must be housed and fed and kept in such a manner so as to maximise growth and minimise stress. Because of this, the young crocs are kept indoors in temperature-regulated houses in dark conditions. Now this is not as bad as it sounds because in the wilds when crocs are young, they tend to gather together in dark places that are moist and warm and close to water. They also gather together in numbers for safety. Knowing this and having been briefed by Dr Huchzermeyer about the warm foetid conditions in the barns, I was still not prepared for what assailed my senses when I entered one of the barns housing young crocodiles.

We walked into a barn containing crocodiles about one metre long, about fifty centimetres short of ideal farming size. These crocs were small enough to handle so we were able to use a croc of this size to demonstrate how to take a blood sample. Inside the very large barn measuring some fifty by fifty metres, there are a number of pens, each measuring about twenty by twenty metres. The pens are concrete and have a shelved concrete floor filled partially with water so that the young crocs can bask on the "banks"

THEY ALSO GATHER TOGETHER IN NUMBERS FOR SAFETY.

THE STENCH THAT ASSAILED MY NOSTRILS WAS LIKE NOTHING I HAVE EVER SMELLED.

partially submerged. They are also able to float in the water in a strange upright position. They stand on their back legs and tail with their front legs and head floating in the water. The light was low and the air uncomfortably warm, about thirty-eight degrees I was told. The unbelievable thing about this entire and very surreal experience is that each pond houses between two and three hundred baby crocodiles. We had to bring lights into the barns to illuminate it in order to have a good look around. The young crocs did not like the light and immediately started to move away from it. We had to be very quiet and any talking was done sotto voce. What I have not yet described is the smell! I have saved that for last in describing the inside of the barn because I need to dwell on it for a while. The stench that assailed my nostrils was like nothing I have ever smelled. Try and imagine the most powerful ammoniac smell. Imagine the filthiest urinal on a very hot day, and multiply that by a very large number and you will have some inkling of the smell that we had to endure whilst working in the barn.

Once, as a vet doing a house visit to an eccentric woman in Brighton, England, I discovered that she kept about one hundred cats in her house and they all lived indoors. They defecated and urinated wherever they liked and the stench was indescribable. Well, the smell in the barn was much worse than that!

Smells notwithstanding, the show must go on and we had to set the adverse conditions aside. Dr Huchzermeyer was not affected as badly by the stench. He had done this before and had mentally prepared himself for it. We took a little while to regain our senses to the point that we could start to work. The human being is however a marvelously adaptable animal and after the first shock we were able to carry on with our investigations.

One of the handlers who works on the farm climbed into the pond near to where we were standing. It was the one nearest to the front door, which stood ajar, allowing a trickle of fresh air to seep inside. He approached the writhing mass of crocodiles carefully so as not to startle them. They did seem a bit anxious and started to move away from him. He had obviously done this before because with a very swift lunge, he managed to grab a one-metre long croc behind the head and around the tail. Thus restrained, the croc immediately gave up the fight and allowed itself to be carried to where Dr Huchzermeyer waited. We then carried the croc outside and Dr H prepared to take his blood sample. There is a large tail vein that runs along the back of the animal and this is the one used to take a blood sample. The handler restrained the croc whilst Dr Huchzermeyer took a hypodermic needle and a syringe and positioned himself behind the croc. The handler then bent the tail down and Dr Huchzermeyer inserted the needle in the correct spot where the tail was flexed. The blood flowed into the collecting tube at a healthy rate and without too much fuss we got our sample.

The sample was sent to a laboratory and numerous parameters were examined. You can tell the health of the herd by taking samples from a few individuals and in this way monitor the herd and make relevant recommendations. Under adverse conditions associated with stress certain bacteria will flourish. If they are detected then it would be safe to assume that the animals are stressed. If they were absent then the converse could be assumed. The whole process took under thirty seconds and the patient was then returned to its pond without suffering any apparent ill effects.

Gratefully we finished our work in the barns and gasping, we stumbled outside. We were then taken to the hatchery where I was shown the egg incubation racks. There were

THE BLOOD FLOWED INTO THE COLLECTING TUBE AT A HEALTHY RATE AND WITHOUT TOO MUCH FUSS WE GOT OUR SAMPLE.

SHE THEN TAKES THE BABIES IN HER MOUTH AND TRANSPORTS THEM TO THE WATER.

hundreds of eggs being incubated. We were told something very interesting here. You can control the sex of the crocodile that will hatch by regulating the temperature of the incubation. At a certain temperature, males were hatched and at another temperature, females would hatch. This means that the genetic potential for both sexes is present in each egg, but depending on the temperature you can choose which sex you wanted. This had some commercial value in that females appear to grow better in the farming environment.

I was given an egg and I found it quite fascinating to examine. Then one of the handlers approached, carrying a baby crocodile that had literally just hatched. This little creature was about fifteen centimetres long and glistened with the fluids that had surrounded it in its egg. It still had a yolk sac and this looked like a small yellow blob underneath the baby croc on its abdomen where the belly button would have been. It was mobile and able to emit a small clicking and squeaking sound. This sound attracts the mother to the nest when the young hatch. The Nile crocodile used to have a reputation for eating their young but this was a misconception made from early observations of their behaviour. What in fact happens is that once the young hatch and even before they hatch and are still in the eggs, they emit this clicking noise. This attracts the mother croc back to the nest and she then digs up the nest and will even crack eggs that are not yet hatched. She then takes the babies in her mouth and transports them to the water. The adult crocs will also defend their young from predators such as monitor lizards who fancy both crocodile eggs and newly hatched babies as part of their diet.

The little creature nestled in my hand and moved about without fear. I hope that it had not imprinted on me. They imprint on the first moving creature that comes their way

and this is usually the mother. In this way a parental bond is established. Well, if it thought I was mother, it was in for a surprise. I marveled that this small little chap would one day grow up to be big enough to make a quick snack out of someone my size.

As we left the hatchery we were told by the handlers that today was feeding day for the adults in the breeding pond on this farm. We were in luck because this was a spectacular sight. The crocs are fed on dead chickens that are obtained from a nearby chicken farm. Any mortalities from the chicken farms are frozen and stored and the crocodile farmers come round weekly to collect the dead chickens and feed them to the hungry crocs. The handlers had two wheelbarrows filled with dead chickens and we followed them to the breeding pond. I followed the handlers into a large enclosure where there was a big pool measuring some one hundred metres across. There did not seem to be anything in the pool, just a still, glassy surface. The handlers parked their wheelbarrows about five metres from the edge of the pond and whistled sharply and loudly. The next instant pandemonium broke out! Adult crocodiles erupted from the pool and came charging hell for leather towards us. They reached the bank of the pond and for a heart stopping moment I thought I was in real trouble but they stopped there and waited. It went through my mind that they were like dogs waiting to be fed and that is exactly what they were waiting for. This ritual had happened so many times that the crocodiles knew the whistle preceded a feed and they also had acquired the habit of waiting for their food on the edge of the pond. The handlers started throwing chickens, the crocs caught in mid air and with an audible gulp swallowed them whole. I had to get in on the action and grabbed a chicken in each hand and tossed them

THE CROCS ARE FED ON DEAD CHICKENS THAT ARE OBTAINED FROM A NEARBY CHICKEN FARM.

THE CROC FLOCK DOC  111

1.   Roy and Dr Huchzermeyer on an island in the crocodile pond.

2. – 4. Sequence of feeding crocodiles with chicken carcasses.

5.   Holding a baby crocodile moments after it hatched.

to the waiting crocs. What I have not told you yet is the size of these animals. They were massive; some in excess of six metres in length and nearly two metres wide. I have fed many animals in my life but this had to be the high point of my animal feeding career. The largest of them consumed about ten or twelve chickens and then seemed to be satisfied. Once satiated the crocs slid back into the pond to cool off and digest. It is difficult to describe the scene. As I have said before, I have had the opportunity of feeding an amazing variety of animals, including sharks, but this experience must rank as one of the great feeding experiences of my life. The sheer size and number of crocodiles that we fed that day, combined with the thrill of the potential danger that these massive animals represented, will be a memory that I will carry to my dying day.

In the space of an hour, I had held a crocodile egg, I had held a newly hatched baby in my hands, I had handled metre-long young animals and I had fed adults so large that they could have made a meal of me.

The path that I have walked in my professional career is a varied and very interesting one. There are many high points and each one makes an interesting story but if I am placed on the spot and asked to try and pick the most interesting experience I have had then the day spent with the croc doc really is up there with the best of them.

Dr Huchzermeyer is an extraordinary man who leads an extraordinary life. I am honoured and privileged to have been allowed to share a day with him.

PAIN IN THE NECK
Cheetah Style

HOEDSPRUIT IS A small bushveld town nestling between the foothills of the Drakensberg Mountains to the west and the Kruger Park to the east. The area has a rich cultural diversity but all the people who live there have a common purpose. They are all involved somehow in the game industry, whether by ownership of land or by performing a service to the people or animals (both wild and tame) living in the area. Hoedspruit used to be the headquarters of the main air defence unit of the 'old South Africa'. Mirage squadrons used to take off and land there. The runways are so long that one can land a large jet without using reverse thrusters. Game animals roam the runways, which of course can be very dangerous for take-off and landing. There is a project underway to use cheetahs to control the game population within the perimeters of the air-force base and keep the runways clear of animals that may cause accidents by getting in the way of landing planes.

Peter Rogers is a wildlife vet living in Hoedspruit and is a good friend and colleague. Peter and I were at university together and both graduated in the same class. We shared many hard years together at Onderstepoort University and we have a friendship that has transcended the years. Peter is fortunate enough to have secured a life for himself and his family living and practising in Hoedspruit. This town is the gateway to the game reserves of southern Africa. It borders on the Kruger Park and has access to all the major and minor wildlife parks. Peter has devoted his entire professional career to helping sick and injured wildlife.

In September 2001 Peter called me and made me an offer I could not refuse. He told me about a cheetah that had a radio collar around its neck. We were going to hunt the cheetah down, dart it, remove the collar and surgically implant a radio-tracking

device into the cheetah's abdomen. This was a very uncommon procedure at the time as the implants were new and state of the art. They are small and once surgically implanted into the animal's abdomen, they do not affect it in any way. The procedure was new to southern Africa, having only been performed once or twice till then. I jumped at the opportunity.

I caught a flight from Cape Town to Johannesburg and then a connecting flight to Hoedspruit. There is always a knot of anticipation in my stomach when I sit down in an aircraft seat on my way to an African adventure.

In September the weather in Johannesburg was warm and comfortable but that's highveld country. We landed at lunchtime in Hoedspruit, which is lowveld country. I disembarked from the plane and I could feel immediately that I was in 'real' Africa. There was a warm dry wind blowing and the light brown dust was stirring on the ground. The colour of the bush is very evocative for me. There is a wonderful poem I once heard. It talks about 'die blou en die blond'. Translated from Afrikaans, this line describes the colours of the bushveld – 'the blue and the blonde'. And that's exactly what the bushveld is like at this time of year. The grass is dry and 'blonde' and the sky is the most beautiful blue. You can't beat the colours and smells of Africa.

The surgery that the cheetah was going to undergo was not an emergency but rather what is called an elective operation. It had been scheduled for the day following my arrival and I therefore had the opportunity to settle in to my lodgings and take the afternoon off to familiarise myself with the territory. We were staying in a tented camp at Kapama, the wildlife reserve where Peter worked.

At the time Peter was employed by the Cheetah Project run by Kapama and worked in a wildlife hospital situated in the reserve. The Cheetah Project's mission is to try and breed

THERE WAS A WARM DRY WIND BLOWING AND THE LIGHT BROWN DUST WAS STIRRING ON THE GROUND.

cheetah in order to restock other wildlife parks. They are so successful that they have the largest captive cheetah population in the world. Since we had the afternoon to ourselves we took the opportunity to visit the Cheetah Project.

Breeding cheetahs has become a challenge not only because of their endangered status, but also due to the fact that many of the animals are sub-fertile and unsuccessful breeders. A few years ago the existing low numbers of cheetah were almost unsustainable and without a successful breeding programme the fate of the cheetah was truly in jeopardy.

We were awake before the first light and with only a cup of coffee and a rusk to fortify ourselves we drove our kombi to Peter Roger's wildlife hospital where we loaded the vehicle and headed for the Karongwe Game Reserve, a private reserve twenty kilometres from Phalaborwa and about sixty kilometres from where we were based. This was where our cheetah lived and this was to be the site of our adventure.

Karongwe offers their guests a truly fascinating experience – a horse safari. Guests can ride in the bush on horseback and having done this, I can recommend it as an excellent way to really explore the bush. The horses do not startle the game and you can get really close to the animals.

The Karongwe Reserve is bordered by tribal trust land, which is land owned by indigenous farmers. This is a danger zone for the cheetah. The tribal landowners shoot any cheetah that stray onto their land as they believe that cheetah will kill their livestock. It is highly unlikely that a fifty kilogram cheetah could take down a fully grown cow so this belief is not born out in reality. A cheetah would certainly prey on calves, however. The chances that the cheetah would stray onto tribal land were also slim as the rangers made an enormous effort to prevent this. In the interest of good neighbourliness, it was

decided to introduce a policy of collaring and monitoring the cheetahs' whereabouts and this was a solution that made everybody happy.

The radio collars were not a good solution for the cheetah, however, as they weighed up to two kilograms and were heavy enough to disturb the cheetahs' balance while hunting. They also chaffed the cheetahs' neck and caused a severe irritation until they became used to collars. For these reasons, and because implants were aesthetically more acceptable from a tourist point of view, we had elected to go for the implant. Don't forget that the main revenue of a reserve like Karongwe is from tourism. A collared animal is jarring to a tourist who has come to see wild Africa.

Our mission was to find the cheetah, dart it, anaesthetise it, remove the bulky collar and replace it with a state of the art battery-powered tracking device, which was to be surgically implanted into the cheetah's abdomen. The cheetah already had a working radio collar around his neck so we were able to utilise the existing radio signal using a hand held radio tracking device. This involved walking through the thick waist high bush following the radio signal.

Kaylee Owen lived on Karongwe and was conducting a research project at the reserve. She was in charge of the collaring and tracking program. Her aim was to discover more about the cheetah's habits and whereabouts. With her help we set off to locate our patient. This should have been simple but this was Africa. The bush was so dense that we could have been five metres away from the cheetahs and not noticed them. I could literally have stumbled over any number of wild animals lying quietly in the bush. There was a true sense of danger.

KAYLEE OWEN'S AIM WAS TO DISCOVER MORE ABOUT THE CHEETAH'S HABITS AND WHEREABOUTS.

I WAS CAKED IN SWEAT AND LONGED FOR WATER.

Often whilst walking through bush tracking a wild animal I have pondered my actions. I have been charged by lions, and an elephant, to name but a few, and have often wished that I were safely back in my house in Bantry Bay. Once the dangerous moment is over though I realize how lucky I am to be a part of all of this. My pulse was racing, not only from the brisk walk but also due to the palpable sense of danger. The fact that an armed ranger accompanied us was a small comfort though.

We stumbled through thick bush trying to locate wild animals that wouldn't exactly have been overjoyed to be found by humans trooping through their domain. The radio collar emitted a signal. We had a tracking device. The device was designed to locate the signal and point us in the right direction. We should have found the cheetahs within a short time. This however was not to be. They are faster than us even when walking through bush and to keep one step ahead of us was no problem to them on that hot and dusty morning. They even stopped to drink at a water hole for a brief moment. We didn't! The heat was getting to us all. I was caked in sweat and longed for water. After about an hour of them leading us almost as though they were playing a game, they settled under the shade of some trees. They too eventually needed some respite. It was at this point that we thought we had our chance.

All through the hour that we tracked the animals, Peter had carried his dart gun, loaded and primed to shoot at an instant. Now, with our quarry settled, Peter stepped up dart gun in hand to try and shoot the dart into our waiting patient. He was familiar with this particular cheetah and knew approximately how much it weighed. This information is important in working out the dose of anaesthetic agent used in the dart. You want the correct dose. Enough to put the cheetah to sleep quickly and keep him asleep for long enough to do the job.

Without too much fuss and with very little noise, Peter carefully tested the wind to ensure that we were downwind. The animals knew we were there but extra precaution could do no harm. Once satisfied that his careful approach would

not startle them, he managed to get within shooting distance. This was about twenty meters in this case. He is left-handed and always looks clumsy with the rifle tucked into his left shoulder but don't let that fool you. He is an excellent shot. With an almost casual air, he lifted the dart rifle to his left shoulder, took aim and fired the dart. Bull's eye, or should I say cheetahs rump. With a sharp sound like air being blasted through your teeth, the pink tasselled dart flew and embedded itself into the hindquarters of the cheetah we wanted. The impact of the dart startled him and he sprang off. We are always concerned that the animal may take flight and run after being darted. They could get lost within seconds of their flight and fall asleep in full sun. This would present a life threatening problem due to hyperthermia from exposure to the sun. With this case however, the radio collar would help in locating him once he was asleep. The dart we used that day contained a combination of two drugs, Domitor and Ketamine. This would put the cheetah to sleep in six minutes and keep him safely down for up to forty-five minutes, enough time to do the job. Fortunately the cheetah only ran a few paces after it was hit by the dart and then settled down under a nearby tree and went uneventfully to sleep

The rangers frightened away the other cheetah with some clapping of the hands and shoo shooing like you would a harmless pigeon in the park. Cheetahs are not generally aggressive animals and it is rarely that they would view a human as food. They hunt animals that are smaller than they are and a human does not quite fit the bill, at least not adult humans. Besides, these cheetahs were used to people. In a private game reserve they do a lot of human watching. It was time to approach the anaesthetised cheetah.

HE LIFTED THE DART RIFLE TO HIS LEFT SHOULDER, TOOK AIM AND FIRED THE DART.

WE MADE ARRANGEMENTS TO MOVE HIM TO THE CHOSEN SITE.

We squatted down to examine the sleeping cheetah. There was some routine maintenance work to be done. The dart had to be removed. We used a scalpel blade to make a small nick just next to the barbed dart. The dart was then gently pulled through this incision and once out, the hole was filled with an antibiotic paste. It is a routine thing for a vet to check his unconscious patient before anything else is done. We performed our pre op check there and then, in the bush under the shade of an African tree. Once we were certain that our patient was stable and soundly asleep, we made arrangements to move him to the chosen site.

We had a mat with handles on either side that we used to carry him to his destination. We carefully placed the sleeping cheetah onto this mat. In the process we had to roll him over. This simple act presented a particular challenge as the cheetah seemed to have a full belly. If one rolls him over whilst his belly is full it is possible for the stomach to twist in the abdomen causing a condition known as a gastric torsion. This is a life-threatening problem that would kill the cheetah if it happened and was undetected. Making absolutely sure that no adverse reactions occurred, the cheetah was gently rolled onto the mat and carried to the clearing where the bush operating theatre had been set up. The vehicles had been brought to the clearing and trestle tables had been set up to act as operating table and instrument trolley. The operating table was padded with a mattress and covered with green surgical drapes that had previously been sterilized.

Even in the bush, basic principles apply. The first thing a vet does with his anaesthetized patient is to carefully monitor him and ensure that all the vital signs are within normal range. We had already done a pre op examination on him. Once he was lying on our bush operating table, this examination was performed again. One can never be too careful. We set up an intravenous drip as a precaution. This ensured that we had a

patent vein that we could use in the event of an emergency. We monitored his temperature pulse and respiration as well. We were now sure that the sleeping cheetah was stable and the next phase of the operation could start. Whilst we were busy getting the cheetah ready for surgery, Phillip, the game ranger was busy removing the bulky radio collar from the cheetah's neck using a pair of pliers to unscrew the nuts and bolts that kept it on. The collar was surprisingly heavy; over two kilograms. This was due to the heavy battery that could last over two years. Holding the collar in my hand I understood how it could have affected the cheetah's ability to hunt. The collar weighed nearly five percent of the cheetah's weight. This would be like me running a marathon carrying a five-kilogram weight. I would not have a great advantage in that particular race. Underneath the collar, his fur was badly chafed and the skin was thickened and hard with calluses. I knew he would be much happier without the collar.

After having the collar removed, we positioned the sleeping cheetah on his back and tied him in position for surgery. This involved being actually tied down with ropes whilst lying on his back with his hind legs drawn into extension so that his belly was clearly exposed. We then used water and soap and a razor to shave all the hair off his belly. The hair is surprisingly coarse and the shaving process is not as easy as shaving my own chin. Once this task was completed, we scrubbed his belly with water and a special sterilizing fluid called chlorhexidine. This is the same product used to sterilize skin in human surgery. Whilst I was busy scrubbing the cheetah's skin, Peter was busy scrubbing his own hands with water and chlorhexidine as well. He then gloved his hands using sterile surgical gloves. I unwrapped his sterile instruments from their transporting wrapping and he inserted his hands into

WE POSITIONED THE SLEEPING CHEETAH ON HIS BACK AND TIED HIM IN POSITION FOR SURGERY.

A GOOD SURGEON ALWAYS HAS SOME BUTTERFLIES IN HIS STOMACH BEFORE A SURGERY.

the sterile wrapping to remove the instruments wrapped in green surgical cloth. All this was done very carefully to avoid contamination. Wrapped up with the sterile instruments was a sterile drape. This was opened and placed over the scrubbed belly. The drape has a square hole cut into it through which the surgery takes place; this is called a fenestrated drape.

This may have been the middle of the bush but no chances or short cuts were taken. Sterile skin, sterile drapes, gloved hands and sterile instruments. Five star treatments for a five star patient who had the distinction of being on the Cites endangered wild life list.

Peter has always sweated a lot and today was no exception. It was quite hot and we had been on a long chase before we actually managed to dart the cheetah. Since darting we had carried him to the bush theatre and there had been a flurry of activity to this point. Now after all had been said and done, it was down to Peter's skills. I half suspect that the sweat was not only due to the heat but also due to a case of pre op nerves. A good surgeon always has some butterflies in his stomach before surgery. Peter however is a consummate professional and once underway, surgical instinct takes over. His hands steady and without any hesitation he lifted the scalpel blade and boldly sliced into the sleeping cheetahs abdomen.

This is not a very complicated piece of surgery. It involves opening the abdomen up and gently inserting the radio transmitter into the abdomen. The implant itself is the size of a piece of faecal material and sits in the caudal part of the abdomen just like a lump of faeces. It is completely harmless and causes no side effects at all. The battery powering the transmitter lasts over two years. Prior to its insertion it had been soaking in chlorhexidine and was completely sterile. To give you some idea of its dimensions, it is about the length of

your palm and if you place your finger and thumb together and make a circle of them, the transmitter will fit through that hole snugly. It weighs about one hundred and fifty grams.

After gently sliding the implant into the abdomen, Peter started to close up the incision using dissolvable sutures in the muscular layer. Suddenly and completely unexpectedly the cheetah seemed to stir and started to wake up. This was very unusual and seemed to be almost an idiosyncratic reaction to the drug used. It is supposed to keep the animal soundly asleep for about forty five minutes. We had only been busy for about twenty minutes and we theoretically had another twenty five minutes to spare. We immediately called for assistance from the people surrounding us who were viewing the surgery. They came and physically restrained the cheetah that was rapidly waking up from its anaesthetic. I dashed for Peters drug box and took out the bottle of anaesthetic agent. Luckily we had set up a drip line so we had instant access to a vein. I drew up a dose of anaesthetic and quickly injected the dose into the now thrashing cheetahs vein. The intravenous dose of anaesthetic is very rapid in its action and within the count of five seconds; the animal once again succumbed to anaesthesia. This was the only time to date that I have seen this happen. The animals always sleep till they are given the antidote but his one woke up half way through the anaesthetic. If it had not been for the meticulous professional preparation done before surgery we may have had a major problem. In its thrashing the surgical sites sterility had been compromised and we had to start to scrub, drape and glove again. Once this was done Peter could proceed with the closure. The muscular layer was sutured closed and once this layer was closed, he used the same suture material in the skin. The suture material is called PDS and takes about forty days to dissolve. The surgery took about twenty

SuDDENLY AND cOMPLETELY uNExPECTEDLY THE cHEETAH SEEMED TO STIR AND STARTED TO WAKE uP.

EVERY ONCE IN A WHILE AN ANIMAL
HAS AN ADVERSE REACTION TO A DRUG.

five minutes from first cut to last suture and that included a ten minute interruption where the cheetah woke up and had to be re-anaesthetized and re scrubbed The surgery had been performed in a sterile way and we anticipated no adverse effects post operatively. Once the last suture was placed, we unscrubbed. Gloves were removed and the drapes taken off. The cheetahs belly was sprayed with a disinfectant and routine antibiotics were administered. The drip was removed and the antidote to the anaesthetic was administered. This would wake the cheetah up within about five minutes.

After the operation was completed we had the opportunity to discuss some of the theoretical considerations as to why the cheetah woke up. There was nothing wrong with the preparations for surgery and the dose of drug was correct. We had to put it down to an idiosyncratic drug reaction. It is a very rare phenomenon but does exist. Every once in a while an animal has an adverse reaction to a drug. Usually the anaesthetic is deeper than planned for the said dose but in this case it lasted for half the prescribed time. Had it not been for the professional preparation and meticulous attention to detail that Peter is renowned for, we may have had a very unpleasant experience of a wild animal escaping from an operating table with a surgical wound still in its abdomen. We were sweating before this little interlude, after its completion we were all soaked with sweat.

After all this has happening, Kaylee Owen switched on her tracking device and tuned it in to the radio implant signal just placed in the cheetah's belly. It was giving out a strong slow signal indicating a strong battery that would last for in excess of two years. The tracking monitor that she used had twenty different frequencies and could be used to monitor twenty animals with radio collars or implants. One just has to tune the monitor in to the frequency of the chosen transmitter. This is an invaluable tool in the bush when trying to locate

Tales of an African Vet

the whereabouts of wild animals. It is also one of the reasons why private game reserves can almost guarantee that their guests will see the "big five" within a short time of arriving at the reserve. This is a well kept secret and if you don't tell, nor will I. It somehow spoils the romance of seeing all these wonderful animals so quickly on the first day of your safari when you know that they carefully monitor the animals' whereabouts with state of the art equipment.

The new implant is invisible to the eye and therefore more tourist friendly compared with the bulky collar which most tourists don't like to see hanging around a wild animal's neck. Eco-tourism helps to finance the reserves and consequently their conservation of wild animals so inevitably a keeping the tourists happy is important

We transferred the cheetah to a shady spot 50 metres away using the transporting mattress with handles again. We then sat quietly and watched him wake up. This was just another successful piece of surgery done in the heart of the African bush. I make light of this as though it was routine for vets to do but in fact all of us who witnessed the procedure were in awe of the level of skill required to perform the entire process with such casualness.

Slowly the cheetah arose, shaking his head. We had to ensure it was safe for his awakening by seeing that there was no other animal round as he regained consciousness. A grudge in a pack of wild animals would have served as a perfect opportunity for an enemy cheetah to take advantage of our patient in his weakened and vulnerable state and tackle him. This is not that unusual an event. If there is a dominant animal that is weakened either by injury or in this case due to recovering from anaesthesia then a subservient animal may view this as an opportunity to kill the weakened animal and then move up in the hierarchy. We guarded him while he took a few tentative steps. The antidote however works quickly and within minutes he was fully awake and striding gracefully.

WE TRANSFERRED THE CHEETAH TO A SHADY SPOT 50 METRES AWAY

Left: *Dr Rogers surgically implaning a radio transmitter into the cheetah's abdomen.* Right: *I am examining the cheetah prior to its surgery. The heart of an athlete.*

The next day we tracked him again just to make sure he had suffered no ill effects from the surgery. We managed to find him and to our surprise we found that he and his friend had hunted successfully. I found this amazing that within a few hours after abdominal surgery the cheetah could hunt. This proved to me once again that it had been a sterile and successful piece of surgery that didn't in any way harm the cheetah. It is also a tribute to the resilience of our fellow wild inhabitants of this planet in contrast to us. Had a human had the same surgery, then the recovery period would be weeks. With a wild animal the recovery period is hours.

We had accomplished our goals. The cheetah's whereabouts would now once again be known and he could be monitored. If he strayed onto tribal trust land or neighbouring farms Kaylee would know this and she would notify the rangers who could then take action to return him to safety

That night our team decided to celebrate at a little restaurant in the old Hoedspruit railway station. The food was good, the wine was palatable, the cigar tasted great but the satisfaction of a job well done was a feeling that I will remember for a lifetime.

A PREDATOR NEEDS both its eyes, nothing less. They need binocular stereoscopic vision in order to hunt successfully. Their eyes are situated on the front surface of their head and they look forward as opposed to herbivore eyes that are situated on the side of the head to gain as much peripheral vision as possible so that they can spot the hunter hunting them and maximize their escape opportunity.

Mehlwane was a lioness on the Thornybush Game reserve situated just outside Hoedspruit. She was the alpha female, head of the pride. She initiated the hunts and very often she was the first lioness to actually hit the prey, taking it down and clamping her powerful jaws round its throat to suffocate it. She was pivotal in the hunting success of the pride. There were young mouths to feed and the lionesses were busy hunting and feeding their young.

For a long time now, the chief game ranger on the reserve whose name was Mike, had noticed that there was a black ring round Mehlwane's right eye. When lying quietly in the heat of the day grooming, they noticed that she continually pawed the eye and it was generally half shut and tears flowed out of it. Clearly there was a problem.

It was decided that the wildlife vet should be called in and the lioness should be examined and if possible treated. Peter Rogers did most of the veterinary work on Thornybush and he was called in to assess the problem. He managed to get to within a few meters of the pride and with the aid of a pair of binoculars he had a good look at the injured eye. His assessment was that there was a congenital problem known as an entropion. This is where the lower lid rolls in towards the cornea. There are small fine hairs on the edge of the lower lid and with the lid rolled in these hairs continually scratch

HIS ASSESSMENT WAS THAT THERE WAS A CONGENITAL PROBLEM KNOWN AS AN ENTROPION.

they surface of the cornea and cause a bad irritation called a keratitis. This continues till the cornea becomes scarred and blue and useless rendering the eye blind. In the process, the animal suffers badly and in the case of a lion, this could even lead to aggression towards people. Her hunting ability would become impaired and she would go hungry. It is then that she may turn towards easier prey like people.

She needed surgery in order to fix the entropion. The only problem is that the condition had not been detected in lions before and although Peter had performed the surgery on a dog once or twice, he was in unfamiliar territory.

He called me and asked if I had done this sort of work before. I replied that I was well versed in the surgery, having performed the operation many times on both dogs and cats. We were then invited to come to Hoedspruit and I would assist in the surgery. This was an invitation I just could not refuse.

We flew in to Hoedspruit via the marvelous airport that I have mentioned before. We hired a kombi and made our way to the Thornybush reserve. Johan, the general manager of the reserve, met us there. He ushered us in to the beautiful lounge in the lodge where we were greeted with refreshments served by white-gloved staff. Talk about back to the colonies. One had the feeling that we had been transported back one hundred years to when the British Empire still thrived and the great white hunters of old were lords of all they saw.

We were taken to our accommodation and the lodge staff carried our bags there. The doors were unlocked and we were ushered inside. The magnificence of the suite I was to sleep in, literally took my breath away. The main room must have been fifty square meters in size, with a huge four-poster bed in the center. There was a lounge area with soft brown leather furniture and a kitchenette with granite counters.

The study area was straight out of the colonial era with a beautiful wooden writing bureau and a leather-backed chair made for the comfort of the person sitting on it. There were two bathrooms, one at each end of the room; one for each of the two guests who were supposed to share this room. Baskets of fruit and flowers adorned the low coffee table and selected Swiss chocolates were placed in small bowls for the indulgence of the visitor. There were big wooden French doors opening onto a patio that overlooked the river and there was a private plunge pool on the patio for the exclusive use of the lucky guests staying here. All this was for me, I was staying in the room by myself for the two days that we were scheduled to stay for. What a pity I was alone.

By the time we had settled in to our rooms it was mid afternoon. It was too hot to go for a game drive so we decided to have a swim in the lodge pool. This was a large deep swimming pool just close to the large thatched patio. We all met there and cooled off for a while. Once refreshed we changed into light summer clothing and met under the thatched roof of the lodge patio. We were offered refreshing cool juices that tasted wonderful in the hot afternoon sun. The patio was also something out of the colonial era. Large ceiling fans circulated the cooler air under the large high-pitched roof. The furniture was once again selected to evoke memories of bygone colonial days. Close to four o clock that afternoon we were served tea. This was our first experience of Thornybush hospitality. I could see from the spread we were offered that we were in for a fat time. The word diet does not exist in lodge vocabulary. There were cream cakes, muffins cucumber sandwiches and many other small delicacies. We were however warned by Johan that dinner would be served at seven thirty so we had better save some space.

IT WAS TOO HOT TO GO FOR A GAME DRIVE SO WE DECIDED TO HAVE A SWIM IN THE LODGE POOL.

IN AMONGST THESE MAGNIFICENT ANIMALS WAS OUR PATIENT FOR TOMORROW.

Once tea was cleared away we had the opportunity to gaze over the river that flowed in front of the patio. There was a large sandy bank and there were footprints of all manner of game on this bank. We were told that night times were the best for viewing game from this vantage point. The bank would be flood lit and the game did not seem to mind.

Mike, the head ranger came and told us that the game drive specially organized for us would leave in fifteen minutes. We went back to our rooms to fetch the various items we needed such as binoculars and bird books. We were hoping to see our patient that afternoon. The game drive vehicle was a 4x4 open truck with three rows of seats. There was also a trackers seat on the left of the bonnet just above the front bumper. Our trackers name was Ocean and we were soon to discover just how sharp his eyes were. We set off on dirt roads and within the space of a few hundred meters the lodge was completely hidden by the thick foliage. Mike was driving and Ocean indicated the way in which we should proceed. He was amazing. We saw bush and dirt; he saw a highway leading to the game animals whose tracks he saw. We drove for a short while under his direction then Mike slowed down because Ocean indicated that there were lions ahead. There, lying under the shade of a thorn tree, in a grassy patch, was a pride of female lions, and in amongst these magnificent animals was our patient for tomorrow. We inched closer until I had a clear view of Mehlwane. The dark ring of tears was clearly visible round her right eye and she was grooming and paying special attention to the eye. She repeatedly licked her paw then rubbed the eye with the wet paw. She constantly blinked and it was clear that she was in quite some discomfort. Mike told us that the word "Mehlwane" meant the one with the eye. She appears to have been like this her whole life and the trackers had given her the name. Well, tomorrow we hoped to fix her. Maybe her name would still be the same but we

hoped that people who saw her in future would wonder why she had the name. We hoped there would be nothing remarkable about her eye after we were finished with her.

The drive took another hour and as the sun was setting we turned round and drove back to the lodge. We saw many other African animals during that hour but my mind was filled with a lioness with a very sore eye and the fact that I would be instrumental in helping to fix it tomorrow.

We arrived back at the lodge and were then once again ushered to the thatched patio for sundowners. We were told that we did not have to dress formally for dinner and that it would be served in the lapa which is a reed enclosed area adjacent to the patio, this is effectively an out door dining room. We went back to our rooms to freshen up and we walked back to the lapa in time for dinner. Instead of a dinner bell, there was a set of African drums that the chefs assistant beat to announce the dinner. The lapa was once again reminiscent of the splendors of the colonial era. We sat at tables covered by white starched linen with crystal glasses and sliver cutlery. The waiters wore uniforms and white gloves. The wine and the food were both superb and the cigars we were offered at the end of the meal were of the highest quality. The bush experience at this level is very sophisticated and designed to evoke the rich splendor of the colonial days. Thornybush succeeded outrageously. As usual, we decided to have as early a night as politeness would allow us to, so once dinner was finished and cigars had been extinguished we headed for bed. We had an early start the next morning.

We were woken at four thirty am with a member of staff politely knocking on our doors. We had fifteen minutes to get dressed, as we were to meet in front of the lodge by quarter to five. I decided to quickly jump into the pool on my patio and once this was done, I dried and dressed and feeling completely refreshed made my way to the parking area.

MIKE TOLD US THAT THE WORD "MEHLWANE" MEANT THE ONE WITH THE EYE.

SIGHT FOR A SORE EYE  131

ALL WOULD BE IN VAIN IF WE DID NOT FIND THE LIONESS.

Peter Rogers was going to perform the surgery that day and he radioed us to tell us that we must go out and track down the lion. Once on to her spoor we were to radio him and he would make his way to us in his vehicle, being guided there by the radio.

Mike, Ocean and other trackers and game rangers greeted us at the car park outside the lodge. There was coffee and the traditional rusks. We quickly loaded our gear onto the game drive vehicles and once we were also aboard, we set off. I always have a nervous knot in my stomach at this time. So much planning goes in to getting to this point. All would be in vain if we did not find the lioness. I need not have worried. We had Ocean on board and he was an expert tracker. It had rained lightly the previous night and this made the tracking easier, or so I am told. To me it looked just as difficult. Ocean however seemed to see large arrows leading to our quarry. Within about ten minutes he said that he had the lioness's spoor. I was hard pressed to believe him but was completely convinced when after an additional ten minutes he pointed to a thicket and indicated that the lioness was there. Sure enough, there she was. I am now a believer in their skills. A good tracker is an essential in the bush. Peter had been informed that we were on to the spoor and he told us he was about fifteen minutes away from us.

We sat quietly in our Landrover, observing the lioness and waiting for Peter. He arrived on time and quietly climbed out of his truck and took his equipment out of his car. He assembled the dart gun and the dart, having estimated the lioness's weight and calculated the correct dose of anaesthetic. He climbed into the front of our vehicle and from a distance of about fifteen meters he shot Mehlwane in the rump. The dart discharged its dose into her and Peter started his stopwatch. It would take about six minutes for the drug to act. We sat tensely in the vehicle and waited. Although the darts impact is quite sore, Mehlwane did not move very far. Within six minutes she was lying on her side and soundly

asleep. The only trouble was that nine other large African lions surrounded her. How were we going to get rid of them? I need not have worried. Mike and Ocean climbed out of the Landrover and clapped their hands and shouted and would you believe it the lions took fright and ran away, as simply as that. Once they were gone, Peter and I walked to our sleeping patient to make sure she was stable and safe. This was the first time that we had the opportunity to physically examine the eye we were to operate on. We saw immediately that our diagnosis was correct and that she did have the entropion we suspected. It was a bad case and would require extensive remodeling in order to fix the problem.

When your pet dog or cat has a surgical problem, you take it to the vet and the operating theatre. When a wild two hundred and fifty kilogram African lion has a problem you bring the operating theatre to the bush

We decided that we would set up our bush theatre under the shade of a nearby tree. We took out a transporting mattress and rolled the sleeping lioness onto it. We then, with the aid of six strong men, carried the sleeping lioness to the designated site. She must have weighed about two hundred and fifty kilograms and all the muscle that we had was needed to move her.

Once under the tree, we set up our sterile operating theatre. This may have been in the middle of the African bush but no short cuts were allowed. The lioness's sight depended on us and we took our responsibility very seriously.

We left the mattress on the ground and brought out our instruments. The lioness would rest on the mattress on the ground and we would squat over her to perform the surgery. I would prefer to have stood next to a table for the op but it was not to be. We had the rangers and trackers assist with the

WE DECIDED THAT WE WOULD SET UP OUR BUSH THEATRE UNDER THE SHADE OF A NEARBY TREE.

THE SURGERY IS ESSENTIALLY A FACE-LIFT.

transport of all the gear whilst we prepared the lioness for the surgery. We shaved the surgical site round her damaged eye and then scrubbed the skin surface with a sterilizing fluid. Peter and I put on sterile gowns and gloves and then opened the sterile packs of instruments and drapes. We then draped off the surgical site and once this was done we were ready to start the operation.

The surgery is essentially a face-lift. There is too much skin forming the lower eyelid. This extra skin allows the lower lid to roll inside. What the surgery entails is to make an elliptical incision in the lower eyelid and remove this excess piece of skin. In the case of Mehlwane the piece of skin was about three centimeters long by about two wide. Once the skin was removed, there is a muscle under the lid called the obecularis oris muscle. This too needs to be transected and a piece needs to be removed. Once this is done, the muscle defect is sutured closed and then the incision into the skin of the lower lid is closed. One estimates the size of the piece of skin and muscle to remove by cutting a small piece out then pulling the edges of the wound together to see how the eye looks. By trial and error the correct size piece is removed. We removed a small piece of skin, pulled the lips of the wound closed and realized that a bigger piece must be removed. After taking a second piece of skin we were happy that we now had enough. We now had to suture the wound closed. We used a dissolving suture material once again because one could not remove the sutures in ten days time without anaesthetizing the lioness again and this is not desirable.

The suture material was thick enough to resist the grooming efforts of a lioness. We also tied many more knots in each suture because the lioness would continue to groom the eye for the full ten days of healing. She may be able to undo a few of the surgical knots but we tied so many on each suture that we felt sure that they would in fact hold the wound closed. This is a technique that Peter has developed over the years and it works well. Very seldom do his surgical wounds break

down. Once finished, we swabbed and cleaned the surgical site and mopped up any small amounts of blood. We injected the lioness with antibiotics and an anti-inflammatory that would also control pain.

Many times in nature, lions fight and inflict awesome wounds on each other. They have a very high threshold of pain and we felt that a small little wound under her eye would hardly bother her but we still administered the pain killers as they have an anti inflammatory effect that reduces swelling and this is beneficial post operatively.

During the entire surgery we had a game ranger with a loaded rifle standing guard over us. Don't forget that we were in wild African bush and the smell of blood from the wound, albeit only a very small amount of blood may have been sufficient to attract the other lions back to their leader. Mike, the head game range seemed to have developed a special affinity for this particular lioness and he squatted with us for the entire surgery anxiously looking on. Once finished, we all relaxed and moved a few feet away from the lioness's head. I took her head in my hands and compared the surgically corrected eye to the normal one. It was remarkable. All evidence of the previous problem was gone. There was some post op swelling by now but this would settle and then the full benefit of the surgery would be evident.

The drug we had used would keep the lioness sleeping for the better part of the day so we moved her into a special crate to wake up. We had the team of trackers and rangers come and help to carry the sleeping lioness to the crate that had been positioned under a shady tree. All precautions associated with full sunlight and sleeping game animals had to be observed. The team grunted and sweated and moved this large cat into the waiting crate. The front door of the crate was a sliding panel to facilitate safely letting her out

DURING THE ENTIRE SURGERY WE
HAD A GAME RANGER WITH A LOADED
RIFLE STANDING GUARD OVER US.

IF THE SURGERY WAS SUCCESSFUL, WE WOULD HAVE REALLY MADE A DIFFERENCE TO OUR PATIENT.

once she was awake. Just before we slid the door closed we had one last look at our sleeping patient to make sure all was well. Reassured, we left her sleeping under the tree in her crate. We were going to return at six o clock that evening to release her.

Many willing hands were there to help us clean up after the operation. Instruments and drapes and surgical gowns were quickly packed away and very soon we were ready to leave the bush operating theatre we had used that morning.

Unbelievably it was still relatively early morning. It was now just after eight and we had been up for four hours. We had worked hard and were now famished. I am amazed at just how hungry this sort of work makes one. Early mornings in the bush followed by hard surgical work with a liberal dose of adrenalin makes one very hungry. We climbed back into the Landrover and headed for the lodge and breakfast. We knew that shortly we would be tucking into a large breakfast and that our hunger would be satisfied.

We arrived back at the lodge within half an hour. We all went to our own rooms to clean up and change into cool clean clothing. Once refreshed and clean, we headed for the patio where breakfast was served. Once again we were not disappointed at what we were served. We still had the entire day ahead of us before we were scheduled to release the lioness that afternoon. We used the time to relax and appreciate the wonders of the African bush. We strolled round the lodge, swam in the pool and read books from the well-stocked library. It was a day of quiet introspection after the surgery of the morning. I am always aware that after the tenseness of bush surgery one needs some quiet time in order to fully appreciate just what we had done. If the surgery was successful, and we were fairly sure of that, we would have

really made a difference to our patient. This is a good thought to dwell on and one needs a few hours of down time to fully appreciate it.

At about five o clock we all gathered in the parking lot and loaded up the gear into the Landrover. It was time to release our patient. There was a quiet tenseness about us as we made our way to where we had left the crate and the sleeping lioness.

We arrived at the spot and Peter and I quickly climbed down and walked over to the crate. There are small ventilation holes that also can be used for viewing the animal inside the crate. We looked inside and could clearly see that our lioness was fully awake. She sat quietly inside and did not seem too stressed. She was not unduly disturbed when we looked inside.

As I said before, the front door of the box is a sliding gate that can be raised and lowered. Our plan was to stand on the box above the lioness's head and then we would slide the gate up and allow Mehlwane to run out of the now open front. I must admit to being a bit nervous at the thought of standing a few feet above a wild lioness with only a flimsy piece of wood between her and me. I expressed my concern to Peter but he said all would be ok. We climbed onto the box and the rest of the crew climbed back into the Landrover. The game rangers had their rifles at the ready and Peter and I unclipped the lock on the door of the crate. We gently slid the door up and opened her way to freedom.

For a few moments the crates door was open and the lioness just crouched there, possibly confused by the sudden sunlight that flooded in. There really was a pregnant pause here. We were all frozen in our respective positions. We on the crate, the crew in the vehicle, the game rangers poised with their rifles and the lioness crouched in the crate.

WE LOOKED INSIDE AND COULD CLEARLY SEE THAT OUR LIONESS WAS FULLY AWAKE.

WE WERE THRILLED AT THE WAY THE EYE LOOKED.

Peter then stomped on the box giving me a huge fright. He must have also startled the lioness because she sprang out and ran off into the bush without even giving us a second glance. I am really glad she was not aware of the tasty human morsels that were so close to her. It was once again a nerve-racking experience in the bush.

We had buried a small digital camera in the bush just in front of the entrance to the crate and had activated it by remote control. We filmed the entire release to try and observe Mehlwanes eye. Once the lioness had moved off, we retrieved the hidden camera and with the aid of a monitor we were able to view the footage. We had a marvelous view of the results of our surgery. We were thrilled at the way the eye looked. During the few short moments when everyone was frozen including the lioness, the hidden camera had a fantastic view of the lioness's head looking directly at the camera. Both eyes were wide open and there was no indication of an entropion. The skin round the eye was black but once the hair grew back and the sutures had dissolved, we were really optimistic that the surgery would be a success.

We left Thornybush the next day satisfied that we had really made a difference to our wild patient. I somehow felt that the job was not completed. We really needed to see her in a few weeks time for a post operative examination. This clearly presented a problem because firstly I lived over two thousand kilometers away and secondly this was a wild lion and she could not be brought in for an examination just because we wanted to see her. This is usually the way with wild animals. One performs the surgery and then unless one is very lucky, you do not have a post surgery follow up consultation. Well, as luck would have it, we were once again called to the area about two weeks later and we decided to contact Mike at Thornybush to see if he knew where Mehlwane was. We were thrilled to hear that he knew exactly where she was and he told us that if we got there that evening in time for the game drive, he would take us to see her. This was great. It is an opportunity not often given to us so we jumped at it.

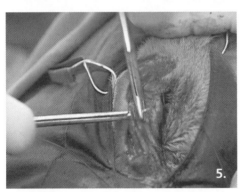

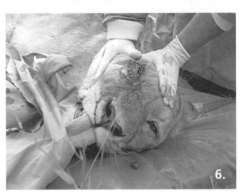

1. Peter darting the Lion Mehlwane.

2. I am preparing the surgical site, shaving and cleaning it.

3. Peter and I performing the surgery.

4. Close-ups of the surgery.

5. We are stitching the wound closed.

6. Both eyes are now open and even.

7. Mehlwane being released in the evening.

SIGHT FOR A SORE EYE

That afternoon we made our way to Thornybush in time for the game drive. We were taken through the bush once again with Ocean as tracker and he found Mehlwane just as efficiently as before. She was lying in the shade grooming herself. She was not paying any special attention to her eye. We had a pair of binoculars with us and I used them to have a very careful look at the eye we had operated on. I was both amazed and thrilled. The only sign of the previous problem was the black ring round her eye. This was due to the hair not having grown back and possibly also due to a lifetime of rubbing that eye and the surrounding skin. This attention to the previously abnormal eye over her entire life may in fact have permanently marked the skin. Both eyes were however fully open and the cornea on the eye we had fixed was clear and bright. She certainly had her stereoscopic binocular vision intact and our alpha female was now back in the business of being a superb hunter.

This story took place in 2001, which is now a number of years ago. We recently came in contact again with Mike from Thornybush. He gave us an update on Mehlwane. Her name has not changed. It is still "the one with the eye". But this is due to the black ring surrounding one eye. The pigment surrounding the previously damaged eye never did go away. One black eye, one normal colored eye but both fully open and fully functional.

HIV/AIDS IS NOT the only scourge of Africa. TB has been around for a long time and has killed many millions of people. Probably more people have died of TB on the African continent than any other single disease including AIDS and only time will tell whether or not AIDS will take over this unenviable record. What is not widely known, however, is that TB does not only infect people. It also infects the wild and domestic animals of Africa and it is fatal for them too. In fact there are two strains of Mycobacterium that cause TB; one is called Mycobacterium Bovis and the other is called Mycobacterium Tuberculosis. Another little known fact is that one of the reasons we pasteurise milk is to kill two specific or target organisms. One is Brucella abortis, a disease causing infectious abortion in cattle and undulating fever in man and the other is the Mycobacterium species, either Bovis or Tuberculosis, causing TB or Tuberculosis. Mycobacterium Bovis is transmitted from infected cattle to humans via the milk and causes about ten percent of TB in humans, the other ninety percent being caused by Mycobacterium tuberculosis. If you drink unpasteurised milk from an infected cow you stand a good chance of contracting TB. If the cows are certified TB free then you can drink their milk safely but if not, you must pasteurise the milk before drinking it. Testing milk cow herds for TB is in fact a major part of a cattle vet's work. The cattle need to be tested regularly to ensure that they are TB free. If they are certified TB free then it is possible to drink raw or un-pasteurised milk but if they are not tested regularly and are not certified TB free then do not even think about drinking the milk. Another fact that I find very sad is that primates that are kept in zoos also suffer from TB. The incidence of TB in these unfortunate creatures is higher than it would otherwise

TB IS NOW RIFE IN THE WILD ANIMALS OF AFRICA AND IT IS A MAJOR PROBLEM.

be for a very strange and sad reason. This strange fact is caused by infected humans actually spitting at these innocent captive animals through the wire fences of their cages. If the animal is hit by the infected sputum, it is sufficient to cause the disease in these captive animals. What a strange thing we humans are.

TB has entered the wild animal population in a very interesting way. Domestic cattle that are infected with TB have grazed with wild buffalo in areas adjacent to the Kruger Park. The buffalo have then become infected through contact with these cattle because the disease is spread via contact with infected saliva or sputum. Grazing on an area that has just been grazed by an infected cow is enough to cause the disease. Infected animals will cough and their saliva can land on the buffalo or the grass being grazed by the buffalo and in this way the disease spreads. The infected buffalo become weak and these are the ones that will more commonly fall prey to a predator such as a lion. The lions eat the infected animal and they in turn become infected. They then spread TB into their own lion population and so the cycle goes on. TB is now rife in the wild animals of Africa and it is a major problem. Death due to TB is now an all too common occurrence. Carrion eaters such as hyenas may also eat a predator that has died from TB. Once this happens, the disease will spread into the hyena population. You can see just how easily this highly infectious disease spreads.

There are programs conducted by the State to try and if not eradicate the disease then at least to control its spread. All wild animals on game reserves that are to be moved from one reserve to another must be tested for TB. If they test negative they can be moved but if they are positive then they must be culled and their herd mates possibly quarantined. Needless to say this is a major problem for the reserve owners and it can have serious economic implications for the game

Tales of an African Vet

reserves. There are programs conducted at various private and State run game reserves to try and breed TB free buffalo and TB free lions. The success of these programs still needs to be determined in the future but the TB problem is one of major proportion and needs vigorous attention.

The population of wild lions on the Thornybush Game reserve had expanded to such a degree that there were now too many lions in too small a place. This often happens due to the remarkable success of the lion as a breeding animal in the wilds. They are successful predators and given sufficient prey on which to feed, they will breed very successfully. Nothing preys upon them and inside the reserve they are not hunted so they breed in peace. Many a time on the reserves the management finds that they have too many lions and this is when they decide to sell off stock to other reserves wishing to introduce this alpha predator into their ecosystem.

Before moving any wild animals, especially lions that may have preyed upon infected buffalo or any other infected game animals, these animals must be tested for TB. This involves a general anaesthetic and the administration of a special TB test.

Four lions living in the Thornybush reserve were scheduled to be sold and had to be tested prior to the sale. If they were negative they could go to their new home but if they tested positive then they would be culled. This is a very serious test with dire consequences for the animals that test positive. Everyone involved is very sombre and tense prior to the testing. If the animals test negative then there is cause for joy and celebration, but if they test positive then the mood is very dark. Magnificent animals strong enough to kill almost any animal they meet in the wilds, except possibly an elephant, are destroyed because of a microorganism too small to be seen by the naked eye. That is true irony.

We started our day very early because even under optimal conditions, finding and darting and testing four lions for TB is a very tall order. Peter Rogers was the attending vet. There were also two other people in the team who specialise in the transfer of

IF THEY TEST POSITIVE THEN THE MOOD IS VERY DARK.

THE PROCESS INVOLVED FINDING AND DARTING THE LIONS AND PERFORMING THE TEST WHILE THEY WERE ASLEEP.

wild animals to their new location. The process involved finding and darting the lions and performing the test while they were asleep. The lions would then be transferred to a quarantine facility where they would wake up. Three days later they are once again anaesthetised and the TB test is read.

The test works as follows. Two strains of TB are administered – one is cattle TB, the other is avian TB. The cattle TB is injected into the skin on one side of the neck and the avian TB is injected into the skin on the other side of the neck. The avian or bird TB acts as a control. If the reaction to the cattle TB is the same size as the avian TB reaction or smaller, then the test is negative but if the reaction to the cattle TB is larger than the avian side then the test is positive. The reactions are measured with a special caliper that measures the thickness of the skin. This is done carefully and it is advisable to have a person experienced in TB testing perform the test. It is also advisable for the same person to read the test from start to finish to ensure consistency.

We set off with the team in two game vehicles. Each vehicle had a game ranger armed and ready to use his weapon in defense of his charges. Peter and my team were in one of the vehicles and the two game capture experts were in the other vehicle. It was thought that if we could locate one or two of the lions they may have success at locating the other two animals and this would give us the chance of actually doing all four lions in one day. As I have said, a very tall order.

The African bush is a strange and wonderful place filled with the unexpected. When you set off to work in the bush, the panorama that unfolds is sometimes more breathtaking and astonishing than anything you could wish for. This was one of those days. Everyone wants to see a lion hunt and successfully kill its prey. This is, however, a rare sighting that very few people have witnessed. Only avid bush watchers occasionally

see this. People who make game their profession sit for days and weeks in order to be lucky enough to capture this event on film. We were driving through dense bush following the tracks of a small pride of lions. The tracker, Ocean, was our guide once again. We had met him on our previous visit to Thornybush when we were here to repair Mehlwane's eye. He remembered us and was pleased to see us. We were hot on the trail of this small pride and according to Ocean the pride contained at least one of the lions scheduled to be moved. We were very close. Ocean was sitting in the trackers seat and directing us with hand signals. We were silent. The animals were used to the noise of the vehicles and did not mind this but were often frightened by voices so silence was the mode we were in just then. Ocean gave the signal for the vehicle to stop and, bending low, pointed just ahead of us. Suddenly a young impala jumped out from the bush about five metres in front of us followed by a lioness. Then from an ambush position just in front of the impala, another lioness came out of the bush at full tilt and pounced upon the hapless impala, grabbing it by its neck. Usually a lion kills by clamping its powerful jaws round its prey's neck and suffocating it. This time, however, there were five hungry lions and they literally ripped the small impala to shreds within the space of a minute or two. I have never seen an animal consumed so quickly in my entire experience in the bush. All that was left within a very short space of time were the two small horns and the hooves. There was a lot of growling and grunting but the lions just kept at it until the impala was but a memory. Within this group of lions there were two of the lions we wanted to dart. I am not sure just how the rangers and trackers knew this but they assured us that two of the lions were there. Peter had prepared a dart just in case we came across the right lion but he needed two at that point. Before he shot one and

SUDDENLY A YOUNG IMPALA JUMPED OUT FROM THE BUSH ABOUT FIVE METRES IN FRONT OF US FOLLOWED BY A LIONESS.

UNBELIEVABLY, THE LIONS TOOK FRIGHT AND RAN AWAY.

scared the others off, he decided to load up a second dart. Once this was done he loaded his dart gun, quietly took aim and shot one of the lions. They were so busy chewing bones that they hardly noticed the sound of the dart gun. The lion that was shot jumped up and growled but did not run off. Very soon it settled down again. Peter quickly loaded the second dart and within a few seconds he had shot the second lion.

We had two lions that would be sleeping within six minutes. Now was the time for the rangers and trackers to try and chase away the other lions. The reasons for this are twofold. The obvious one is that it is safer to work on sleeping lions when the conscious ones are at a safe distance. The other reason is that it is possible that one of the lions may have a grudge against one of the sleeping lions and if this were the case now would be a good time for the grudge to be settled. This would involve a lion that is fully awake attacking one of the sleeping or nearly sleeping lions. Clearly this would be a very one-sided fight with dire consequences for the sleeping loser.

How, I asked myself, were the rangers going to chase away three large lions? I was only allowed to speculate for a short time. They climbed out of the car, clapped their hands and chased the lions away as though they were chasing a few small dogs. Unbelievably, the lions took fright and ran away. This left our two darted lions who were already groggy from the drug and too sleepy to be frightened away. They lay down in the bush and within six minutes were asleep.

Now that it was safe we climbed out of the game vehicles and prepared for the TB test to be administered to the sleeping lions. We had already decided that they would be transferred to a quarantine facility nearby and Peter radioed the other team to come to us and load the lions onto their vehicle. Whilst they were on their way over to us, we got to work.

There is a lot of record keeping in a TB test. The skin fold thickness is measured prior to the test being administered. This is done with a special set of calipers. The avian TB is then

administered intradermally on the right side of the neck. An intradermal injection means that the injection deposits the fluid inside the skin and not under it. The skin of a lion is about five millimeters thick so one is able to inject the fluid into the skin. After this is done the bovine TB is injected on the left side of the neck. The measurements of the skin fold thickness of each side are recorded along with the date and time of the test and the animal's name. This simple procedure was performed on both lions and I acted as secretary by recording all the information in a dedicated notebook. By the time we had finished, the other game vehicle had arrived and we decided to load both the lions into the back of this vehicle. An adult lion can weigh up to three hundred kilograms and it takes a team of strong men to lift a sleeping lion into the back of a "bakkie". It was a strange sight seeing two sleeping lions in the back of a regular open bakkie. Once loaded they were driven off and we were left to find the other two lions. With the load they were carrying I am sure that if they were stopped in a speed trap whilst driving on the open road, the traffic officer would think twice before giving them a ticket!

We had been lucky with the first two and had found them quickly. We'd started out at five in the morning, it was now seven and we were ahead of schedule. We climbed back aboard the game vehicle and set off to try and find the tracks of the other lions. I have no idea how Ocean was able to distinguish between lions just by their tracks but the rangers assured me that he in fact was able to do this. We drove back and forwards across our path, cutting from side to side to try and pick up the other lions tracks. After half an hour we had still not found anything worth following and decided that the bush telegraph system would now be called in. It was getting warm by this time of the morning.

Thornybush is a working reserve with many guests being driven round in as many as eight game drive vehicles at any one time. Each vehicle has a tracker and a ranger and they are equipped with radios.

WE HAD BEEN LUCKY WITH THE FIRST TWO AND HAD FOUND THEM QUICKLY.

ONE OF OUR POTENTIAL PATIENTS HAD BEEN SPOTTED AND WE WERE GIVEN DIRECTIONS.

The head ranger named Mike was driving us around. We had worked with him as well when we repaired Mehlwane's eye. He radioed his colleagues who were scattered all over the reserve and told them what we were looking for. Once this was done, it was just a matter of time before one of the vehicles spotted our lions. Whilst we waited Mike suggested that it was coffee time. We could hardly fault the suggestion. It is amazing just how hungry and thirsty one gets working in the bush. A thermos of coffee was produced and passed round and we were given those marvelous enamel mugs that hold a large volume of coffee. You can actually drink your fill this way. It was a special moment – coffee sweetened with condensed milk and rusks to eat. Who could ask for anything more at seven in the morning in the bush?

Suddenly the radio crackled to life. One of our potential patients had been spotted and we were given directions. We started the vehicle and drove off in the direction we were given. About fifteen minutes of rough bush driving later we met up with the ranger who had spotted one of our quarries. He indicted to us where the lion was and then drove off with his load of guests. It was not really a good idea for the paying guests to see what we were going to do even though they groaned loudly at being left out of the action. Ocean was called in to examine the tracks and he pronounced that it was in fact one of the lions we wanted. He sat in his tracking chair and directed us to where the lion lay. It was a solitary young male lion, about three quarters grown. He was lying in the shade and looked as though he too had just fed.

Once again Peter was called in to administer the tranquilizing dart. Over the years of doing his job, he had become quite good at guessing the weight of the animals that he treated. This is important in order to work out the dose of anaesthetic

agent needed for the dart. Our partially grown male was examined visually and Peter determined the dose taking into account his full belly as well. The dart was quietly fired into the recumbent lion's rump. The impact is quite hard, and hard enough in fact to cause this particular lion to spring up in alarm and run off into thick bush. We had six minutes to wait but we were concerned that he would run into an area that was inaccessible. If this happened and the animal was not found it would be left lying in the full sun. Hyperthermia would set in and this is life threatening. We immediately followed the startled lion and with Ocean's help we were able to keep track of him until he went down. Once down we approached him. He appeared to be soundly asleep but this little illusion was soon dispelled when we tried to move him. He raised his head and growled. He was very groggy and his reactions were very slow but his teeth were sharp and the weight of his head driving them into human flesh would be enough to do terrible damage. We had to administer another top-up dose of anaesthetic. This was not an error but actually an idiosyncrasy of darting animals that have just fed. One often errs on the conservative side. Better to have a patient that is not fully asleep but quiet enough to work with and give a further dose to, than to have a patient that is too heavily doped and in a life-threatening situation.

We performed the same procedure on him that we had done for the previous two lions. We now however had a dilemma. We needed to find the fourth lion but could not leave this one lying asleep in the bush even with a guard. The other vehicle was was not due back for another hour. We decided to load him into the back of Peter's vehicle and take him to the quarantine station ourselves. Time really was not on our side. Administering the TB test took close to quarter of an hour. The loading took close to a quarter of an hour. The drive to the quarantine station and back was going to take

THE DART WAS QUIETLY FIRED INTO THE RECUMBENT LION'S RUMP.

WE HAD THREE LIONS CAGED AND TESTED. at least an hour and a half. The other team had not yet returned from taking the first two animals to the quarantine station so the chances of finding the fourth lion that day seemed to be diminishing rapidly. We would have to make a judgment call soon as to whether or not we would be able to locate and test the fourth lion. We loaded number three and drove off with him. I sat in the back to tend to him whilst he slept.

The drug that we use to immobilise lions and keep them sleeping sometimes allows the animal to wake up but still be heavily sedated. I was not expecting this because this lion had already been given a top-up dose but the well-grown youngster that should have been soundly asleep suddenly raised its head and looked at me. I nearly jumped out of my skin with fright. I need not have worried because after the effort of raising his head, he just flopped back. I was not to know this however and my pulse went through the roof. There was not a lot of space in the back of the open bakkie and we were traveling fairly fast. If I had needed help, it would have been difficult to attract Peter's attention. But as I said, he just flopped down and went back to sleep. I had not called for Peter's help so luckily my dignity remained intact.

We eventually arrived at the quarantine station and with the assistance of quite a number of people working there we transferred our sleeping patient to his temporary cage. Time had passed and the sun was now a significant factor. We had three lions caged and tested. We would have about a two-hour window tonight to try and find number four. This was our best course of action.

Once this decision was made we stood the teams down till evening. Mike invited us back to the Thornybush lodge for one of their fantastic breakfasts and we could not pass up this invitation. By the time we arrived back, most of the guests had returned from their game drives and were busy starting their breakfasts. Their curiosity could not be satisfied and Mike was asked by a number of them what was going on. It was an educational opportunity and he took it. He explained

the implications to them of the disease called TB and I think that once he had finished his explanation, there were a few more people in the world that were sensitive to the wild and understood the massive problem that TB posed to the African wildlife.

The breakfast was as sumptuous as ever and after what I considered to be a marathon eating session we went back to our sleeping quarters to recover from the early morning's exertions. We still had the evening work to look forward to so we decided to get some rest. Peter left us to complete his rounds and we made arrangements to meet up at four that afternoon. From mid morning to late in the afternoon, the bush can be an inhospitable place. It can be hot and sometimes, just before the rains come, it can be very humid as well. Sometimes there are high clouds and the sun seems to be magnified through the clouds. It was one of those days. All you could do during the heat of the day was lie around in the shade and pant and sweat. I empathized with and felt sorry for the animals in the bush. They too were finding whatever shade they could and were also panting to keep cool.

Four-o-clock came slowly but eventually it was time to meet up again and try and find lion number four. If we could locate this last lion we would really have done a good day's work. We climbed aboard one game-driving vehicle and Mike activated the bush telegraph once again. He radioed the other vehicles that were just setting out for their afternoon drives and told them what we wanted. We set out at four and hoped that we or one of the other vehicles would soon spot our lion. We drove around the area that this particular lion hunted in but could not find him. Despite the fact that we were on a job looking for a specific animal it is still a great pleasure and privilege driving round in the African bush. We saw a female elephant and her very young calf; we spotted buffalo and many of the small to medium-sized herbivores

IT WAS TIME TO MEET UP AGAIN AND TRY AND FIND LION NUMBER FOUR.

A QUICK ESTIMATE OF THE LION'S WEIGHT AND THE DART WAS MADE UP.

that populate the vast African plains. Don't forget that even though these farms are privately owned and fenced, they still represent the vastness that is the Southern African Wilderness. The only difference between now and a few hundred years ago is that the wilderness areas have been parceled up and fenced. They are, however, expanding as more and more landowners turn their land over to private game reserves and stop cattle farming. Interestingly enough the wilderness areas of Southern Africa are growing.

Suddenly our radio crackled. One of the other rangers had spotted what he thought was our last lion, about twenty minutes drive from where we were. It was now after five and even though it was summer, the sun was setting just after six o clock. It was cutting it fine but we felt that it was worth the effort to try. Mike drove us as quickly as he could to the location and within the twenty minutes estimated for the journey we arrived. Ocean was once again our tracker and he located the lion quickly. Both Ocean and Mike confirmed that this was in fact the right lion and Peter quickly prepared his dart gun. A quick estimate of the lion's weight and the dart was made up. As usual, he shot the lion with very little fuss and bother. This shot, however, was a difficult one because he had to aim through a thicket of trees. But his aim was excellent and the dart hit the lion in the shoulder, a perfect shot. Startled, the lion ran off but soon settled down. Luckily we did not lose sight of him because he only ran for about one hundred metres. He then lay down and within six minutes he was asleep.

I had now helped in three TB tests and this was my fourth. I was an old hand by now and within five minutes of this lion falling asleep we had administered the test. Next we loaded the sleeping lion onto the back of the bakkie and we set off for the quarantine station. The drive would take forty five minutes and it was already quite dark. Once again I sat in the back with the sleeping lion while we drove as fast as we safely

could. This time there were no surprises and the lion slept all the way without moving at all. When we arrived we once again assembled a team to carry our sleeping patient to the cage that would be his home for the next three days.

I stood back to survey the work we had done that day. There in front of me were four wild African lions in various stages of sedation and anaesthesia. We had managed to capture them all and perform the TB tests we had set out to do. They were all caged in the quarantine station waiting to have the results of the test read in three days time. Only then would their fates be known. In the meantime we had a tense wait ahead of us.

We decided to have an early night. The day had been hot and busy and we were all tired and grateful for the opportunity to get some sleep.

The next day I drove to visit the caged lions in the quarantine station. I opened the enclosure where the cages were and walked slowly towards them. I knew that the drugs had worn off by now but I was not prepared for what greeted me. I got to within about five metres of the cages when suddenly all hell broke loose. All four lions charged the bars of their respective cages and the gale of sound that assailed my ears was unbelievable. The volume of their roars from close quarters was enough to stun me almost senseless. I thanked my maker that the bars that stood between them and me were strong enough to withstand their charges. Thoroughly frightened, I hastily backed out of the enclosure. Peter in the meantime had come to see what all the commotion was about and had a quiet little chuckle at my expense.

I stood a safe distance away and quietly observed the four lions pacing their cages. The cages were in fact big enough to house each one for a few days. There were two compartments to each cage and experienced handlers used hosepipes and water to encourage the lions to enter one compartment of the cage. Once this was done a strong gate was used to keep the lion in its compartment while the other compartment was cleaned. The lions were fed by placing meat in the clean section.

Sometimes three days can pass very quickly in the bush when you are game watching. This time, however, the time seemed to ooze excruciatingly slowly by because we had to wait the three days to find out the results of the tests. We all wanted to read the tests but we had to wait the mandatory three days to validate the test. I never thought it was possible to be so impatient for the days to pass.

No matter how slowly time passes, it does eventually pass and the three-day waiting period came to an end. We assembled at the quarantine station with feelings of anticipation and dread. It really was a nerve-wracking time. Depending on the outcome of a test that I had played an intimate part in, the four lions would either go on to new homes to hunt and breed and do what all good lions do or they would not be allowed to wake up from the anaesthetic. These magnificent creatures could die.

Each lion was in its own cage and had been starved for 12 hours prior to the administration of the anaesthetic dart. They roared and charged the bars as Peter approached them. He was used to doing this and did not flinch. I had had a small taste of the enormous gale of sound they produce so I was primed for their fury. The volume of noise that these four lions produced was awe-inspiring. Peter had a small dart gun that operated via compressed air and using this he surreptitiously administered the anaesthetic dart to each of the roaring lions. Once injected, they still continued to make an enormous volume of sound for about three minutes, then the drug kicked in and they started to get drowsy. They lay down in their cages and uneventfully went to sleep. Once down, Peter and I climbed into their cages and using the special calipers that are designed for TB testing, we measured the reactions on either side of their necks. It must have taken us about twenty minutes to finish reading the tests.

Relief flooded through the entire crew as we announced that all four lions were TB free and they could be certified as such. This enabled them to be moved to their new homes. The tension of the last three days melted away and was replaced by a quiet sense of relief and peace. There would be no euthanasia today.

Left: *Peter is darting one of the lions before TB testing.* Right: *I'm treating the small wound left by the dart after removal.*

The two people who specialised in game transfer were part of the audience and had come prepared for the eventuality of a negative test. They had a large closed truck in which the four lions would easily fit. They also had individual transport crates for each lion. Once they knew the results they sprang into action. Each lion was individually crated and the crates placed onto the back of the truck. Once safely packed the lions were driven to their new homes, about two hours from where we stood.

It is mandatory for all game animals to be tested prior to moving them from reserve to reserve. The consequences of taking a chance are horrendous. The reserve could be TB free prior to the introduction of a new animal. That new animal, however, could be the vector that brings TB to the reserve that was otherwise TB free. It is beyond belief that there are still people in the game industry who have a very casual attitude to TB. They try and get away with not testing for TB; alternatively they try and tempt the vet with financial incentives to "fudge" the tests. Luckily my profession is an honourable one and the vets take their professions and their jobs very seriously. Dishonest vets are few and far between. The profession takes TB very seriously and with a lot of hard work and a bit of luck, this disease that is decimating the wildlife of Africa will be brought under control. I am proud to have played a part, albeit a very small part, in controlling and eradicating TB from the wildlife of Africa.

THE STRANGE THING about us humans is that when we discover that animals can get the same conditions and diseases as us, we are surprised. Many a time I have had owners express amazement that their animals developed heart failure or cancer or liver kidney or other organ failure. Even I was surprised, however, when I discovered that fish, which are at home in water, can actually develop the bends or a disease known to aquatic vets as gas bubble disease. Simply put, these fish develop gas bubbles in their blood and tissues due to reasons that I shall expand upon later.

My friend David Huchzermeyer is a vet. His father and mother are vets, his wife is a vet and his grandparents were vets. Talk about a genetically preprogrammed vet! Well, David had the odds stacked against him for any other profession. Not only did he become a vet, but he also followed in his father's footsteps and became a very unconventional one. His father is a world renowned crocodile, ostrich and bird vet as well as having a healthy interest in tortoises, and David is a world renowned fish vet. Talk about unconventional vets. David and I had been in contact and that is when I was introduced to fish with the bends. He invited me to join him and observe him in action in a very interesting case. He consults for a fish farm in the Leydenburg district where there was a very special problem. Fish were suffering from abscesses on their skins and the various vets who had been called out were at their wits end to try and cure the problem. Antibiotics had been administered but to no avail. That is when David was called in. He is a smart boy, our David, and he not only examined the fish but had a good look at the farm, the water supply, the management, the feed and any other factors that could play a role in the health and well-being of the fish on the farm.

I flew to Johannesburg and hired a Kombi to drive us there. Leydenburg is about four or five hours drive from Johannesburg depending on how fast one travels. We set off for Leydenburg at four am and drove like bats out of hell. By just after eight am, with nerves quite frayed from the speed that our driver drove at, we arrived at our destination. We had called David at about seven that morning to give him our estimated time of arrival so when we arrived in this small town, which is the centre of the aquaculture industry in South Africa, we drove to his veterinary hospital and met him there. I had not seen him for about fifteen years but was surprised at how little he had changed. He still looked like the twenty-five-year-old young man that I remembered from university. He did, however, have an air of professionalism and competence around him that was missing when he was younger. Since our gear was already loaded in the Kombi, he said that he would travel in his own vehicle and we would follow him. I decided to travel with him and get some background information to the problem.

Whilst driving, David told me that fish on this farm had been dying for a number of years and the farmer was in quite some trouble by the time David was called in. Up to thirty percent of production was lost each year and the farmer could not sustain another year like this. Many vets had tried to make a diagnosis but none so far had been successful at diagnosing and treating the problem. Most of the time the vets had thought that there was an infection in the water and numerous antibiotics had been prescribed but all to no avail. The antibiotics are administered by dosing the water that the fish swim in. David came in with a fresh set of eyes and more knowledge about fish that anyone else.

The water supply for the farm came from a waterfall that cascaded down the mountain for hundreds of feet before landing in a catchment pool. By the time the water landed in the pool, rocks that stuck out in its way had broken it

WE SET OFF FOR LEYDENBURG AT FOUR AM
AND DROVE LIKE BATS OUT OF HELL.

TOO MUCH OXYGEN WAS BEING DISSOLVED INTO THE WATER.

up. The water also fell hard into the pool resulting in super aeration. Then, to add insult to injury, the pool was quite high above the ponds that the fish were kept in. There was a feeder pipe taking water to the ponds and the shutoff valve that regulated the water levels, was at the top of the pipe. When it was shut at the top of the pipe, there was a column of water still in the pipe, sort of hanging there from the shutoff valve. This super aerated water was then subject to a negative pressure effect of being suspended in a column. The net result was that too much oxygen was being dissolved into the water. In semi scientific terms, the pressure of the oxygen in the water exceeded the pressure of the oxygen in the air just above the surface of the water. This excessively oxygenated water was "breathed" in by the fish through its gills and once in the blood stream, the excess oxygen had nowhere to go other than to bubble out of the blood and form little bubbles in the gills and tissues. The result of all this was a fish with the "bends". It took David quite a while and lots of thorough investigations to make the diagnosis.

If the diagnosis was correct then the treatment based on that diagnosis should cure the problem. David made recommendations based on his diagnosis and observations and once these were instituted the problem cleared up. His recommendations were simple. Take the gate valve from the top of the feeder pipe and put it at the bottom. That way, instead of water "hanging "from the top of the pipe, it would be pressing down on the valve at the bottom of the pipe and the excess oxygen would technically be "squeezed out" of the water so that when the fish breathed the water, the amount of oxygen in it would be correct. This simple solution caused all the problems to clear up. Production rose by thirty percent and David went from zero to hero. A very important part of treatment on a production farm is routine monitoring and on a weekly basis, David was called in to monitor the trout on the farm. We were accompanying him on this weekly visit. There were still one or two fish per week that succumbed to the bends but this was an acceptable and almost normal event. Provided that the numbers were kept in this range, all was well.

We arrived at our destination and climbed out of the vehicle. I looked around and was totally mesmerised by the beauty of the place. There were dozens of large round ponds, each one measuring about twenty metres in diameter. These ponds were about one metre deep and each one was filled with different sized fish, from fingerlings measuring a few centimetres in length to fully-grown trout referred to as table size, ready to be harvested and eaten. The ponds had green lawn surrounding them and the entire farm was at the foot of a cliff two hundred metres high. Cascading down the cliff was the offending waterfall. The only trouble was that the so-called offending column of water was breathtakingly beautiful.

I work as a vet in the city of Cape Town. To be fair, the view from my practice has to be one of the greatest views in the world. I look over Table Bay and the city of Cape Town from the windows at the back of my practice and I look at Table Mountain and the associated mountain ranges from my reception area. I am spoiled, but the environment that David works in with beautiful views of farmland and waterfalls and gorgeous pools of fish glittering like diamonds in the sunlight sure comes a close second.

How does one monitor a fish? Well first you have to catch it, and then you have to immobilise it to take the specimens that you need. Then you have to return it unharmed back to its environment. Let me tell you how this is done.

Fish can actually be anaesthetised for up to a minute or so and once asleep they can be removed from the water and worked on. You add a special anesthetic agent to the water and wait while the fish swims around. You can tell when the fish is unconscious because it lies on its side. When this happens you can remove it from the water and take your

I WAS TOTALLY MESMERISED BY THE BEAUTY OF THE PLACE.

specimens. David added the anesthetic agent to a large bin filled with water and then added one trout to the water then we waited and watched. Within a few moments the fish was lying on its side. After wetting his hands well, David swiftly removed the fish from the water and placed it on a damp towel. He then took a pair of scissors, snipped a small piece of gill tissue from underneath the gills and then took a microscope slide and gently scraped mucus off from the fish's skin. Only a small amount of mucus was removed because if you remove too much of this slimy body covering, you can really harm the individual. The policy of doing minimum harm when examining any individual is employed here. A quick visual inspection of the entire fish was performed to ensure that there were no external ulcers and then the fish was returned to a bucket of fresh water with no anesthetic agent in it so that it could wake up and be returned to the pond to join the other fish.

The specimens thus taken were then examined. The small snippet of gills was squashed onto a microscope slide and covered with a cover slip and it and the mucus slide were examined with a microscope. Interestingly enough, if there are gas bubbles in the blood, they can be clearly seen in the gills when examined under the microscope. In addition, if the fish is sick, there will be parasites on the skin that would not be there in a healthy fish. Although the entire process took just under a minute, the results of the examination were a sensitive barometer to the health of the pond. You look at a few fish from the same pond and from this you can infer that there either is or is not a problem in that pond. Herd health implies that you examine a few individuals from the herd, flock or in this case pond, in order to make inferences about the health of the entire group of animals that one is monitoring. The individuals that we examined were in fact healthy so the pond that we were examining was given a clean bill of health. David spoke to the owner of the farm and reported his findings to him. There seemed to be no problems that day.

Well, we had heard about gas bubble disease, we had seen how environmental factors could cause the problem and we had witnessed the monitoring of the health of a pond but we

had still not seen an example of gas bubble disease. David finished his work on the trout farm and then told us that our next port of call was a koi farm a few kilometres away. There were individuals there with active cases of gas bubble disease. In addition to this, there is a philosophical difference between a trout farm and a koi farm. In the trout farm situation the individual animal may sometimes be sacrificed in order to make a diagnosis and in a pond of several thousand fish, one fish more or less is of little consequence, as hard as that may seem. In a koi farm, however, individual fish may be worth up to one hundred thousand rand and there is no sacrificing of individuals for the sake of the pond. Each fish is an individual and gets the full treatment. At this koi farm, there were active cases of gas bubble disease and these fish needed treatment on an individual basis.

The koi farm was about half an hour's drive from the trout farm so we all climbed into the vehicles and set out. The Leydenburg district has a plethora of fish farms. They farm fish for food there as well as for sport and some of the best trout runs in the country can be found there. The other aspect of the farming enterprise there is the koi farm. These farms breed koi for sale to the general public as pets. They make amazing pets and owners tell me that each fish has a personality of its own. They can be tamed, hand fed and will actually respond to individual signals. I have known of koi that come when called. They also nibble at fingers and some like to be stroked. The scenery was very beautiful with the Drakensberg Mountain forming the backdrop and our drive passed quickly.

Unlike the trout farm, most of the ponds on the koi farm are indoors. This is to ensure a constant environment, which will optimise survival. These fish individually have great financial worth and are treated very well. If an individual fish gets sick, it is isolated and monitored and treated with the best medicine possible, usually by a fish specialist. That's where David comes in. He is a fish specialist and is often called out to handle koi.

EACH FISH IS AN INDIVIDUAL AND GETS THE FULL TREATMENT.

EACH POND SEEMED TO HAVE A DIFFERENT SIZE OF FISH IN IT.

The owner of the farm and his manager met us. They showed us into a large barn-like structure. To my surprise, once we were indoors, it was quite hot and humid. The temperature of the air and the water was kept constant. I was surprised by what we saw once inside the barn. There were dozens of ponds, each one measuring about three by three metres and about three metres deep. Each pond seemed to have a different size of fish in it. I was told that they are divided up into age groups and females were kept separate from males. The females lay their eggs on artificial branches, which are left in the pond once the eggs are laid. The males were only allowed into a pond to fertilise the eggs and once this was done the adult fish were removed and the fertilised eggs were allowed to hatch without the presence of adult fish to prey off them. This ensured optimum survival of the hatchlings.

We were guided to the pond furthest from the entrance that seemed to have the largest fish in it. Their colours were spectacular. Individual values are determined by the size of the fish and the rarity and pureness of their colours. The fish we were there to treat was about three quarters of a metre in length and had a magnificent orange and white skin. The white was very white and the orange was like a setting sun. The manager of the farm used a special funnel shaped net to capture the fish. It was allowed to swim head first into the canvas funnel and once securely in, the net was quickly lifted out, and the fish gently decanted into a waiting large bucket of fresh water. David added what he estimated to be the right dose of anesthetic to the water and we waited for the fish to go to sleep. And we waited and we waited. After about ten minutes the fish was still swimming sluggishly and was definitely not unconscious. Don't forget that a sleeping fish will lie on its side. David thought that even though the capture process was gentle, there might have been some stress causing adrenalin release. This would counter the effect of the anesthetic thus necessitating a higher dose. Reluctantly he added a bit more to the water and we waited for a few more minutes. This time the fish did go to sleep and within an additional two minutes our patient was lying on its side sleeping. The manager of the farm wet his hands and quickly but gently removed the fish from the bucket. They told me that this fish weighed about five kilograms. He placed it on a wet towel and David called me over to show me what gas bubble disease looked like. He gently turned the fish onto its back and just beneath the gills there were two ulcers, one on each side. They were red raw patches about five centimetres wide. The skin was broken and raw and the lesions looked very sore. Clearly this fish needed treatment.

Now how, you may wonder, does one apply topical treatment to a fish that swims in water? Well, David has used technology and an existing product to solve this problem. Baby diapers have a clumping agent in them that forms a gel when wet. Using this very substance that forms the gel, he adds his antibiotic and other remedies to the powder that forms the gel and then applies this to the ulcers. Once the powder is wet, it forms a sticky gel that stays on for hours in the water. The medicines are then absorbed and can help the fish. I wonder if the inventors of this product that is so widely used in the diaper industry ever envisaged that their baby nappy product would be used to treat sick fish.

David applied the powder to the fish and ensured that it was wet and had clumped and stuck to the slippery skin. The fish by now seemed to be waking up and started to wriggle. Then with a flip of its tail it effortlessly shed the hands that restrained it and tried to jump back into the water. David told us that the fish was actually so strong that without the help of the anesthetic, there was no way that we could have restrained or treated the fish.

NOW HOW DOES ONE APPLY TOPICAL TREATMENT TO A FISH THAT SWIMS IN WATER?

THE CAUSES OF GAS BUBBLE DISEASE ON THE KOI FARM DIFFERED SLIGHTLY FROM THE TROUT FARM.

Due to the chronic nature of the problem, the fish needed numerous applications of this special powder. David told us that he comes to this farm once a week to treat and monitor affected fish. The prognosis is fairly good in that the fish treated in this way generally make a full recovery.

The causes of gas bubble disease on the koi farm differed slightly from the trout farm. Management issues seem to play less of a role and there seems to be susceptibility of certain individuals to the problem as opposed to entire ponds being affected. It is not rife on the farm but due to the value of the individual, they have to be treated.

After finishing the treatment we packed up our gear and prepared to leave for our drive back to Johannesburg. We still had a four-hour journey ahead of us and were anxious to start. The owner of the koi farm however invited us to have a quick refreshing cold drink with him before we left. He had been kind enough to allow us to observe David at work there so we felt that the least we could do was to accept his invitation. Whilst enjoying his refreshments at the farmhouse he told us an astonishing story.

The farm used to have many of its ponds outside. Some of their largest and most valuable fish lived in these ponds. Aesthetically this seemed to be a good option. The ponds were large and the fish had the opportunity to live a more natural existence, being outdoors and exposed to fresh air, sunlight and nature.

One night apparently, a few years ago, there was a violent storm and lots of lightning and when the staff arrived in the morning they found one of the large ponds filled with dead fish. All the fish in the pond had been killed and they had what looked like burn marks on them. The diagnosis eventually made was that lightning had struck the pond killing all the fish in it. This was a tragedy, not only of great financial

1. David and I taking specimens from a sleeping fish; 2. David looking down a field microscope, examining the specimens; 3. Making friends with the farm dogs; 4. Removing a valuable khoi prior to treating it.

proportions but some of these fish were the tamest and oldest fish on the farm. The owner had actually befriended some of these individuals and he and his family wept for the death of these magnificent animals.

So now they are all housed in doors. Away from nature but also away from the elements that sometimes can cause such a cruel blow.

We finished our refreshing cool drinks and climbed aboard the Kombi for our ride back to Johannesburg. Four hours later we were back. Tired but exhilarated from our adventure. I felt enriched to have been a part of this adventure. I had learned something amazing that I hope will astonish you as much as it did me. Fish, like all other living creatures need air to survive and to my and I am sure your great surprise, these aquatic creatures can suffer from the same debilitating and sometimes deadly disease that deep sea divers get, namely the "BENDS".

THE FISH WITH THE BENDS

WHEN WORLDS COLLIDE

WHEN A DOG bites a snake and then the snake bites the dog back, only sadness prevails. This story has a sad start, a sad middle and an even sadder ending. I hope something can be learned from it.

Let me start at the beginning.

My good friend Braam Malherbe is the snake man of Cape Town. You have no doubt seen the crocodile hunter on TV. This crazy Australian does outrageous antics with reptiles. He is not unique. Braam is well versed with reptiles and his handling ability easily rivals the Crocodile Hunters. Whenever there is a snake or any other reptile that is injured, Braam is invariably called out to assist. Amazingly, since first writing this story, Braam has become the first person on planet earth to run the Great Wall of China in one go. That's 45 kilometres per day, every day for four months. I am privileged to know him.

On the particular day that this story happened, Braam was called out to the Northern Suburbs of Cape Town. There is a green belt there where people walk their dogs. The dogs are usually let off the lead but owners should be vigilant because there are snakes in the area. Some of the snakes are very shy and will retreat quickly when a dog gets near. This is a good thing because some of these snakes are also highly poisonous and do not take kindly to barking dogs. Owners should always have leads handy and if the dog appears to be barking frantically at something in the bush, they would be well advised to call the dog to heel and put the lead on. Unfortunately the owner of the Staffordshire bull terrier who was one of the tragic role players on the day did not have a lead handy that day. His dog was barking frantically and despite being called many times the dog continued to mock charge and rush into the bush. Suddenly there was a frantic growling and snarling and the dog rushed into a small thicket and attacked something there. Then with a yelp, it jumped back and appeared to be in great pain. Cautiously the owner approached the bush and saw a coiled up snake. The dog had attacked and bitten the snake and in self-defense the snake had bitten the dog back. If only a lead had been handy and if only the owner had acted more rapidly. But these now were all empty wishes. The owner recognised the snake and identified it as a Cape cobra. These are particularly deadly snakes and this one was a full grown adult about one-and-a-half metres long. They bite their prey and inject their lethal venom into their victim via small very sharp teeth as opposed to the Egyptian cobra that spits venom at its prey. They are also shy and non-aggressive, choosing to flee from danger rather than confront it. Their needle-sharp small front teeth inflict a particularly painful bite and when they bite they inject a neurotoxin that paralyses respiration quickly and induces heart failure. Within a short time the dog was in deep distress and despite being rushed to the vet, it died.

The first instinct a person has after having one's dog attacked by a snake is to try and kill the snake. This owner, however, was different. Possibly he accepted some culpability in the matter in that he did not have a lead handy. Possibly he also realised that had he called his dog away more firmly, the dog might have listened to him. Instead of trying to kill the snake, which would have been a dangerous thing to attempt to do, he called Braam.

Braam drove out to area and learned that the dog was dead. The strange thing is that the snake still lay where it was found. It had not tried to move. This in itself was strange behaviour. As I said before, they are shy animals and will try and escape from confrontation if possible. Braam used his catching instruments to fish out the snake safely. These are long tongs, almost like braai tongs. They enable you to

WITH A YELP, IT JUMPED BACK AND APPEARED TO BE IN GREAT PAIN.

BRAAM CAREFULLY EMPTIED THE SACK ONTO THE FLOOR AND THE ADULT COBRA WAS DECANTED OUT.

capture the snake's head and hold it firmly. After trapping its neck in the special tongs, Braam was able to restrain the snake with his hand and examine it. There was a bite wound about half a metre from the snake's head and the snake appeared paralysed from below the bite. The dog had bitten the snake and caused damage but he was not sure just how much.

I had treated quite a number of cases for Braam. The patients were varied and very interesting. I had treated any number of snakes, guinea fowl, iguanas, small mammals, rodents and birds for him. It was my policy to usually treat the wildlife that he brought to me without charging. I did it out of interest and was never disappointed. All the cases that I have seen with him are fascinating. He called me and told me that he was bringing the snake to my practice for me to examine and treat if possible. He placed the snake in a bag and tied the top firmly shut and accompanied by this dangerous cargo he rushed to my practice.

He arrived late in the afternoon and carried the bag into my prep room. It was here, at the heart of the practice, that most of the hospital work is done. Braam carefully emptied the sack onto the floor and the adult cobra was decanted out. Before any examination could take place the snake had to be restrained and once again his catching tools were employed to restrain the snake. Braam was then able to grab the snake's head firmly between his fingers and thumb, in this way keeping its mouth closed and ensuring that it was controlled I was then able to examine the wound and felt with my fingers that the snake had been bitten near the spine. There were also broken ribs at the bite site.

A dog is a powerful creature and a bite from a staffie can inflict terrible injuries. What we needed here was an x-ray to determine the extent of the wound and the damage to the

spine. I felt that a sedative would not be a great idea because the snake was already severely stressed and depressed and the sedative would just exacerbate matters. Braam undertook to hold the snake whilst I x-rayed it.

We dressed Braam in a lead apron and helped him put a lead glove on. He had to keep one hand free in order to hold the snake's head but was able to cover the free hand with the gloved one so as to protect himself from the x-rays.

We positioned the snake below the beam of the machine and placed it on an x-ray cassette. I set up the correct factors for the x-ray and once this was done and all was ready I pressed the button and fired off the machine. We took two exposures, one from the side and one from the top. In technical terms these shots are called AP and lateral views. I then asked Braam to remove the snake and took the x-ray cassette to the dark room to develop it. The entire procedure took a few short moments and the developer took just ninety seconds to develop the x-ray film. I came back from the dark room with the developed film and placed it on the light box for examination. What I saw was not very promising at all.

Besides having a number of ribs fractured the snake had a fractured vertebral column or spine. This was clearly seen on both the views. The spine is a series of bones called vertebrae. There is a hole in each vertebra through which the spine runs. Effectively the bones form a long bony tube in which the spinal cord runs. If there is a fracture of the bones of the vertebral column then there is often disruption or severance of the actual spine. This is a very severe injury and usually the patient is paralyzed, mostly for life. In this snake's case, the spine was completely severed from the bite of the dog. This snake would be paralyzed for the rest of its life.

We discussed the results of the x-rays and the various options that we had. Braam has a herpetarium and over the years has kept many injured snakes. He has rehabilitated them and successfully released them back into the wilds. This option was discussed

BRAAM UNDERTOOK TO HOLD THE SNAKE WHILST I X-RAYED IT.

THE ONLY THING LEFT TO DO WAS TO EUTHANISE THE UNFORTUNATE ANIMAL.

but in the end discarded as I felt that the chances of this snake regaining the use of its lower body were pretty much zero. We could liberate the snake back into the environment as it was and let nature take its course but this option was also discarded, as it was completely inhumane to do this. In addition to being inhumane it was also potentially very dangerous because even though the snake was semi-paralyzed, it was still very poisonous and given the fact that it now could not escape, it would become aggressive and even more dangerous.

The only thing left to do was to euthanise the unfortunate animal. Once we had made this decision I asked Braam to restrain the snake once again and I drew up sufficient euthanasia drug to do the deed. I usually try and inject snakes in the heart. I used a stethoscope to locate the heart and once this was done, I injected five millilitres into its heart.

Within a short time the snake was dead.

Lying there still, with eyes that had dulled in death, there was an air of melancholy that was almost palpable. This should never have happened. The dog was dead, the snake was dead and all could have been avoided. I know that there is a lesson here somewhere but I don't want to preach it. You conclude it for yourself.

Once the snake was still and at peace, Braam decided to use it to explain numerous things to us. The snake was dead but still deadly. Even in death, if one accidentally allowed the teeth to prick an unprotected hand there is sufficient venom on the tooth itself to cause a problem. Carefully using a steel forceps, Braam opened the mouth and showed us the very sharp and remarkably small teeth with poison dripping out of the tip. The actual tooth is hollow, like a hypodermic needle. The snake bites its victims and injects poison into the prey via the hollow needle like small teeth. Once the prey is dead, the snake swallows it whole. These snakes usually prey on rodents

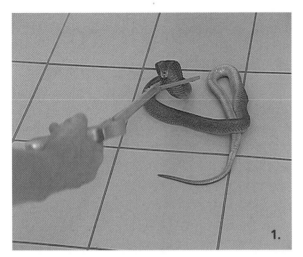

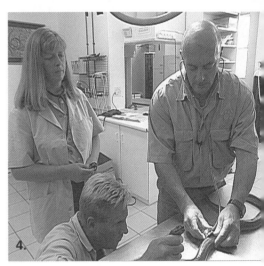

1. Using capture tongs, Braam delivers my patient; 2. We are about to X-ray the snake; 3. The fracture is clearly visible on X-ray; 4. Locating the heart prior to euthanasia. Braam and my wife are looking on.

and other pests and if not for the remarkable success of the snake as a rodent control measure, our domestic environment would be overrun by rodents. There is a place in the ecosystem for all of the living creatures on this planet.

We had to dispose of the body now that the snake was dead. Braam felt that the correct thing to do was to return it to the wilds for nature to take its course. I felt that this was a good idea but the only thing that concerned me was that I did not want some animal or even worse some child to discover the corpse

THERE IS A PLACE IN THE ECOSYSTEM FOR ALL OF THE LIVING CREATURES ON THIS PLANET.

and possibly get injured. We decided to find a secluded place on the mountainside and place the body under a bush where decomposition would occur rapidly. We placed the dead snake in a sack and drove up the slopes of Lions Head to the top parking lot. From there we hiked the rest of the way to a secluded spot far away from the paths that are used by people and animals. Once we were happy that the spot was safe we found a bush and tipped the dead snake out underneath it. We made sure that it was well covered by the bush and we left it there.

I glanced up and looked around at the mountainside and was struck by something that I had not really focused on till that moment. What I saw was as follows. There was a clear line between the houses occupied by man and the wild area occupied by nature and its creatures. This line was so obvious that day. It is a line that is often crossed. Man ventures into nature and sometimes wild animals enter man's domain. Whenever there is a clash between wild animals and man or his pets, there should be respect. With respect there can be co-existence. Without it there can be only tragedy. Man is the intruder here. We cross over the borders into the domain of our fellow wild animals. We have occupied the mountainside. We are also the so-called intelligent species. It is up to us to set the example of how to cohabit with other species. If we do this with sensitivity then we will all survive. If we do not, our fellow inhabitants of this planet will be harmed and we will be the poorer for it.

MOVING WILD ANIMALS from place to place is both a science and an art. These seemingly hardy animals easily succumb to stress and often die due to the stress and trauma of capture and translocation. They need to be handled with great care and sensitivity in order to maximise their chances of survival when being caught and moved from one location to another. There are some capture outfits that chase their prey into capture nets and then physically manhandle the animals into vehicles. Needless to say their success rate is rather low. Game animals are susceptible to a disease called "Capture Myopathy". This occurs when the animals are severely stressed due to the capture process. Lactic acid builds up in the muscles to the point that it becomes fatal. The animals then die due to the stress of capture. The other possibility is that they are stressed but do not die immediately. Rather what happens is that the stressed animals are immune compromised and they become sick and debilitated a few days after they are translocated. This is known as "Translocation disease". The best way to move an animal around is to involve a veterinarian. These skilled professionals have dedicated their lives to the wellbeing of this precious resource. They know how to tranquilise the game and move them in a way that maximises their chances of survival. This is a story about a gemsbok that was moved to a new home. The vet only became involved late in the process.

Professor Dave Meltzer was the head of the Wildlife Department of the veterinary faculty of the University of Pretoria, commonly known as Onderstepoort. This is a world-class faculty situated sixteen kilometres north of Pretoria. The drive through Pretoria is always beautiful in spring. The city is known as Jacaranda City because of the profusion of these beautiful purple trees lining the streets throughout the entire city. Towards the end of

ONDERSTEPOORT. THIS IS A WORLD-CLASS FACULTY SITUATED SIXTEEN KILOMETRES NORTH OF PRETORIA.

September, the jacaranda blossoms start bloom. This is usually the signal for students at the University of Pretoria to start studying. It is a common saying at Onderstepoort that you learn in your first year. If you are not studying when the Jacarandas start to bloom then you risk failing the year because you have left your studying very late. The Veterinary Faculty is staffed by some of the best vets on the African continent and wherever vets who have qualified from this faculty go internationally, they are welcomed with open arms. Some of South Africa's most successful export commodities are here skilled graduates. They have carved an excellent name for themselves throughout the world wherever they work.

I called Prof Meltzer to ask him if there were any interesting cases in or around Pretoria. Like all the clinical departments, the department that he heads up has an ambulatory clinic servicing the surrounding area and if there are problems and clinical cases within a fifty kilometre range of the faculty then they usually send out a vet to treat the sick animals. These vets take students with them and the experience gained via the ambulatory clinic stands us in excellent stead for the future.

He introduced us to Dr Melvin Quan, a postgraduate veterinary student studying a master's degree in Wildlife. Melvin had been called out to a farm near Pretoria where a small gemsbok herd was having difficulty settling in to their new environment. The farmer had purchased the animals from another location where the ecosystem was different to the one the animals now found themselves in. It is uncertain how they were captured but one thing was for certain, a vet was not involved in the initial capture. It was not outside the realms of possibility that the animals were herded into capture nets with no sedation or tranquilisation. This method involves herding the animals into bomas made of nets. They become entangled in the nets and are then wrestled

down to the ground and manually hoisted into trucks. The herd was then transported to their new home. This further stressed the animals, as they had to adapt to new grazing and their new environment. It seemed as though all the stress of capture and translocation was causing a problem. Their immunity had become depressed and this rendered them susceptible to various diseases as well as external and internal parasites. This is a common problem in wildlife that has been moved from one farm to another. The problem can be and very often is life threatening and rapid intervention is necessary to help the individuals affected in order to ensure their survival.

We met Melvin at about six in the morning. We took half an hour to load the vehicle and set out to the game farm,, which was about fifty kilometers west of Pretoria. We drove through the outskirts of the city in September in early spring. The jacarandas were just coming into bloom. There had been little rain that winter as the area was a summer rainfall area. The bush was dry, dusty and brown. The purple blossoms from these marvelous trees that were just starting to flower added a magnificent splash of colour to an otherwise drab color scheme. Rain usually comes to the bushveld in summer and then the fields are transformed into lush green pastures that are bursting with life. For now however, dust prevailed.

We arrived on the farm at about seven. Whilst this may seem early, by wildlife standards it was not. Usually one would want to be on site at daybreak. Early is good when working with wildlife. This is an important point because when working with game, it is crucial to ensure that you do the work in the cool of the morning to avoid the heat of the day. When an animal is darted with most anaesthetic agents, the unconscious animals lose control of their ability to regulate their temperature; their thermoregulatory mechanism. This is a side effect of the drug

A SMALL GEMSBOK HERD WAS HAVING DIFFICULTY SETTLING IN TO THEIR NEW ENVIRONMENT.

used. Mammals are warm blooded. This means that their body temperature is kept constant despite the external temperature. When the anaesthetic agent dissociates the ability to keep the body temperature constant then the animal's temperature can soar if left in the sun and death can ensue very quickly due to hyperthermia. When darted, the animal does not instantly drop unconscious. It can take about six minutes before sleep ensues. In that time, an animal that has just been shot with a dart can panic and run and believe me, sometimes trying to find a wild animal in the bush with a six-minute head start is impossible. These animals can then fall asleep in full sunlight creating a life-threatening situation. Six minutes in the hot African sun is sufficient to kill. Early is good, late is bad.

Once on the farm, Melvin assembled his dart gun, a crucial piece of equipment in any game interlude. The dart gun is a specialised piece of equipment that fires a syringe loaded with an anaesthetic drug. The syringe is designed to inject a predetermined amount of the drug chosen for the job into the target animal. Once this is done, there is a time lag until the animal goes down. Some of these dart guns work with compressed air, some work with a small firing cap and some even work as a blowpipe where the operator uses air expelled from his lungs in order to shoot the dart. Different systems have been evolved to suit almost every occasion. On this occasion, Melvin had a compressed air dart gun that was accurate to about fifty metres.

It took about ten minutes to assemble the dart and load it into the gun. Great caution has to be taken when using the various drugs associated with game capture. We too are mammals and we are particularly susceptible to some of the drugs used. A small amount of drug spilled onto mucous membranes such as the mouth or a drop into the eye and you have whole lot of trouble. You need an antidote to the drug nearby and a competent assistant trained to inject the antidote into you in case you get some of the contents of the dart in your eyes or in your mouth.

At the end of the dry season in September, the bush was reasonably thin and finding our sick patient was not too difficult. Melvin had his dart gun assembled and loaded with

a syringe containing M99, a game capture drug and a drug that man is also highly susceptible to. Now all he needed was for the Gemsbok to stand still in an area where the trees were thinner so that he could get a shot off. This, however, was the tricky part. As soon as he tried to approach the gemsbok, it would stumble off into the bush. I pointedly say stumble because it was clear that he was a sick animal and he had lost his vigour. There was no spring in his step and it was all he could do to in fact move away from us. Each time he moved, we would follow; the farmer with his open land rover and Melvin and I on foot. The time was now closer to eight and the sun was warming the air. We were getting tired from marching through the bush. Each time we thought we had our chance we were disappointed because just as Melvin would take aim, the Gemsbok would once again take fright and move off, albeit slowly. Eventually we must have tired the Gemsbok because it lay down underneath a tree and allowed us to approach. Melvin had a clear shot from about thirty metres and fired off the dart. But would you believe it, there was a small branch about two metres away from the Gemsboks rump and the dart stuck in the branch. I decided to try and retrieve the dart and slowly sneaked up to the animal. I was able to actually get close enough to retrieve the dart and back away without disturbing the Gemsbok. What I did not know then, but have subsequently learned is that this great achievement was not due to my incredible stealth and delicate movements but due to the animal being so sick that it was near death. Unfortunately Melvin did not seem to know this either. I gave the dart back to him. It had not discharged its drug and Melvin was able to use it again. He reloaded the dart gun and then he tried to sneak up on the animal and dart it. He too was successful and was able to get within a few metres of the animal before shooting the dart. Our

THE GEMSBOK BECAUSE LAY DOWN
UNDERNEATH A TREE AND ALLOWED
US TO APPROACH.

Our HAPLESS GEMSBOK RECEIVED A DART IN HIS RUMP.

hapless Gemsbok received a dart in his rump and stood up and once again stumbled off into the bush. We followed on foot knowing that within about six minutes the drug would have taken effect and he would be down. There was no great challenge in keeping up with him, he was too sick to really get going and within a short while he settled down again. There he stayed, lying on his chest under a shade tree.

Within the prescribed time our patient went to sleep and we wasted no time in examining him. This was just another illustration of our inexperience. The first thing that should have been done was to secure the animals horns. They can be lethal if the gemsbok was still even slightly awake. One toss of his head and we could have become a kebab. This is extremely dangerous and these long horns can inflict a life threatening injury to the uninitiated. We live and learn. These animals can appear to be asleep but when startled, they can suddenly toss their heads making life very dangerous.

We began our examination with a general inspection of the Gemsboks skin and hooves. We noted a heavy tick burden, dehydration and infected fetlock joints as well as probably a heavy worm burden. There were wounds and scratches on his skin as well. These are all typical signs of translocation sickness where the animals immunity is depressed rendering it susceptible to external and internal parasites. This causes debility, dehydration and the animals stumble through the bush and are often injured by branches and thorns that they would normally avoid if they were healthy and strong. Subsequent to all this is death. If this was a small animal like a dog or cat, I would have given it intravenous fluids and tried to rehydrate it. This can be done in an extensive situation as well but Melvin elected not to do this. He poured on a topical tick preparation, and we administered an injectible dewormer. I suggested that we give the gemsbok some antibiotics and I also felt that a shot of steroids would do no harm. After all this was done, we had to administer the antidote

to the sedative, a drug known as M50/50. The blood pressure of the animal was low so it was difficult seeing and hitting a vein. The antidote had to be given intravenously. This is where the small animal vet comes into his own. We have to be able to give a kitten an intravenous injection so hitting a vein in a Gemsbok was no big deal. We raised an ear vein and I gave the animal the antidote into this vein. Within a few minutes we could see consciousness return but unfortunately our patient was so weak that it could not rise. It lay recumbent on its chest and looked very debilitated. It did not even try and rise and this really was a grave sign. In hindsite the poor animal was doomed before we even started but where there is life there is hope and at the time we felt that trying to treat it was worthwhile.

It is a cardinal rule that one should not leave an unconscious patient in the care of a layperson. However, had to travel back to the faculty and there were deadlines to meet. We had no choice other than to hand over the patient to the farmer. Once we were assured that our patient was awake, albeit not ambulatory, we took our leave. The gemsbok had still had not risen and this was not a good sign. Usually the animals get up within a short time of the antidote being administered. We gave the farmer instructions about caring for the patient. It was important that the animal stay in the shade and it was also important that it should rise, eat and drink before the day was done. We had done the best we could and now it was up to the farmer to implement our instructions but more importantly, it was up to nature to take its course.

The next day our Gemsbok was dead.

In retrospect, there was so much that we could have done. This was my first interlude with a wild animal and I have learned much since then. First principals apply, no matter how large or small, tame or wild the animal is. If it is dehydrated, drip it. If it is in shock, treat it for shock. Identify the problem, make sure of your diagnosis and treat specifically. I am not sure we could have saved the gemsbok, but I know that we could have given a better account of ourselves and I felt that given the opportunity to do it again, armed with hindsight, we could do it better.

Left: *Melvyn and I examining the sick Gemsbok.* Right: *Prognosis poor, our patient would not get up after the antidote was administered.*

It is always sad when a patient dies. I have a thing about this. I don't believe that any creature should die alone. Whether it is a wild animal or a domestic pet, if I can, I want to give my fellow creature comfort in its dying moments. I am not sure if it really makes a difference but I can say anecdotally from many hundreds of times that I have done this that I think the poor departing animal knows that I am there and somehow receives comfort. I was saddened by the Gemsboks dying and was also saddened that it died alone. I know that many animals die alone but I had a part in trying to help this one and would have preferred to be present for its final moments of life. Possibly I would have been able to give it something. Possibly it is I who would have benefited. Who knows? I just don't think that living creatures should die alone.

Death is a part of the vet's job. Sometimes we administer last rites to our departing patients and sometimes we are actually called upon to euthanise the patient. Fortunately, more often than not, the patient lives and there is an ending that one can smile and feel good about.

I look back on the gemsbok with mixed emotions. I was glad to have been given the opportunity of helping but sad that we were not able to acquit ourselves better. Each little experience however is cumulative and the mistakes that we made acted as good lessons for the future. Next time I know I will do better.

Tales of an African Vet

THE WORD 'GAME' has a number of different meanings. In the context of this manuscript, game refers to the wild animals that roam the plains of Africa. If one talks about sport, then the word game refers to the playing of the sport. Playing the game can also mean cooperating with someone or something. Being game to do something implies being willing or cooperative. The game ranger is all of the above and so much more. He is the marshal and custodian of the wildlife on our continent. He is a player of sport with such physical dedication that he is able to hike the plains of Africa with ease, often walking marathon distances daily in his patrols. He is willing to go not just the extra mile, but also the extra hundred miles. He is also a very 'game' game ranger, prepared to do whatever it takes to get the job done and secure the outcome. These wonderful individuals are indispensable in the wildlife world. They are the unsung heroes of the wildlife industry.

This is a story about a game ranger whose name I do not even know. I heard it from a vet who I worked with who took part in the adventure. It is a story about all the definitions above and some that defy definition. In order to write the story I going to give this ranger a name. This name is of course fictitious and represents all the game rangers, male and female, black white or coloured, those that were, those that are and those that will be. The ranger's name is Adam.

The sun was large and red and low on the horizon. It was almost the end of a hot and dusty day towards the end of summer. Adam had been out since before dawn and was looking forward to getting back to his modest home. He had

THE SUN WAS LARGE AND RED AND LOW OVER THE HORIZON.

decided what he would eat that evening and had also decided to treat himself to a mug of coffee, possibly laced with a small shot of brandy and sweetened with honey. He would enjoy a quiet hour on his stoep listening to the sounds of Africa and retire to blissful slumber. He was driving his patrol vehicle, an open land rover and was about half an hour away from getting back. There was a small kopje about one hundred metres ahead and on impulse he decided to stop there, switch off his engine and just observe the bush and listen to its sounds for a few minutes before heading home.

At the top of the rise he killed his engine and switched the volume of his radio unit right down to enjoy the silence. He sat there savoring the sounds of Africa at dusk. The grazers would still graze a bit before settling down for the night. The daytime animals would be heading for their holes and lairs and the nocturnal animals would be getting ready for their business of the night. The panoramic cycle of life that has repeated itself for countless years would do so yet once more tonight.

His ears were sharp, having listened to the sounds of the bush for many years. He spent a lot of time in solitude and this also honed his instincts.

The hair on his arms and at the nape of his neck suddenly stood up. Something was wrong. He listened carefully for the sounds that must have registered first in his subconscious. There it was. It sounded like hyenas making a kill. But there was something else; another sound, a squealing sound that

he could not identify. Hyenas prey on anything they can but usually end up eating carrion. The sounds were coming from the east. That was to his right as he sat in his car. Something was definitely wrong. He knew it as surely as he knew his own name. He quickly started his Land Rover and headed for the sound, all thoughts of home forgotten.

He guessed that the sounds were half a kilometre away. That would take him about five or six minutes negotiating the bush at dusk. As he got closer, it became easier to locate the actual spot because the sounds increased in volume. The sounds were coming from just ahead, behind a thicket. He

HE SAT THERE SAVOURING THE SOUNDS OF AFRICA AT DUSK

swung the vehicle round the thicket, expecting the hyenas to disperse at the sound of the vehicle. But as his headlights illuminated the ground behind the thicket, he knew that his instincts were correct.

There were six hyenas surrounding a baby rhino that could not have been more than five or six months old. They were charging the baby and nipping its flanks and limbs. In turn it was defending itself with ferocity beyond its tender age. A six-month-old baby rhino can weigh up to three hundred kilograms and can still present as a formidable foe. One butt from its head with its little horn bud can fracture ribs and break limbs. Even though it was outnumbered and outgunned, it was not a pushover and the hyenas were taking no chances. Up until Adam's arrival, the end would have been inevitable but now things were different.

THERE WERE SIX HYENAS SURROUNDING A BABY RHINO

Adam drove straight for the hyenas and hooted. He hoped this would scare them off and give him a chance to try to save the little

animal. The hyenas, however, were not easily deterred and only backed off a few meters. The little rhino stood its ground and did not run from the vehicle. It turned around and Adam was able to get a glimpse of its other flank. There seemed to be a large piece of intestine hanging out of a gaping wound. Something strange had happened here. Where was the mother? Adam positioned his vehicle between the hyena and the baby rhino and kept the engine running. By revving it and hooting and flashing his lights he was able to keep the blood hungry hyenas at bay. Thoughts of his own safety never crossed his mind. Six hyenas could easily have made a meal of a game ranger. They are not man-eaters but given the opportunity, who knows for sure.

Multi-tasking comes naturally to a game ranger and now Adam had to put that skill to use. Whilst revving the motor and flashing the vehicles lights, he switched on his radio and called into base. He described the situation and asked for help. The vet would also be needed because it looked like an emergency operation was required. All this time the little rhino stood its ground, still making the squealing sounds that Adam first heard and thought so out of place. The little fellow was also game in his own way and kept on mock charging the pack of hyena that stood just outside the beams of light made by the vehicle's headlights.

Help was about an hour away and a routine of sorts was established to keep the situation under control. The motor was running and the lights were flashed regularly. Adam kept the vehicle between the rhino and the hyenas. A stalemate developed. The hyenas kept a short distance away and the baby rhino, somehow realizing that Adam and the Land Rover represented some sort of safety, kept his distance but ensured that he was on the far side of the vehicle. Even at this tender age he sensed that he should keep the vehicle between himself and the pack of hungry hyena.

And this is how they were found an hour later. Two other game vehicles arrived with game rangers and trackers and vet Dr Peter Rogers. They all climbed out and looked at the scene in amazement. 'Why didn't you use your rifle Adam? one of

ADAM KEPT THE VEHICLE BETWEEN THE RHINO AND THE HYENAS...

the rangers asked. 'Because the hyenas have a right to their lives as well', was Adam's reply. 'I also thought that if I fired at them I might have scared the baby away and then all would have been lost. I doubt that I would have been able to find and save the little guy in the dark. As it is, I think I was just in the nick of time.'

Whilst this short conversation was going on, Peter had estimated the rhino's weight and assembled the dart he was going to use to immobilise the baby. He quietly took aim and shot the rhino in the rump. Six minutes later the baby was sleeping and they had the chance to examine him and see the extent of the problem. There was a gaping hole in his flank, and a deep puncture wound into his abdomen.

From this wound a loop of intestine hung, which had been dragged in the dirt. Peter set up a drip because the little creature was showing signs of dehydration. The staff then moved the baby onto a clean tarpaulin that would have to serve as an operating table. Peter prepared his instruments and drugs and took out a twenty-five litre container of water to scrub his hands and the wound. Using the water and a sterilising fluid, he set about his task.

The wound really looked like a gore wound from another rhino horn. It was possible that a male rhino had tried to mate with the baby's mother and in the process gored the baby. Where was the mother though? Perhaps the injured baby took fright and ran away. We will never know what happened.

By this time the drip had been running for a few minutes and the wound had been cleaned and sterilised. It was now time to replace the loop of intestine and suture the hole closed. This required Peter to take the loop in a gloved hand and stuff it back through the hole in the animal's flank. While pushing the loop back into the abdomen, he checked along its length for necrosis and puncture wounds.

SIX MINUTES LATER THE BABY WAS SLEEPING...

THE LITTLE RHINO
SEEMED QUITE HAPPY
TO DRINK FROM A
VERY LARGE BOTTLE.

Amazingly, even though the loop had actually dragged along the ground, it was remarkably undamaged, just dusty and a bit dry. Once the loop was back inside Peter was able to attend to the actual gore wound. He used a thick piece of suture material to close up the internal layers of the abdomen and then used the same material to close up the skin. Even though this was a baby, it was a member of the pachyderms. These are thick-skinned animals and suturing their skin closed requires quite some effort.

This was done quickly and efficiently and all that was now left to do was to bandage the wound, administer antibiotics and drugs for shock and remove the baby to safety. It had been decided to take the baby rhino to Peter's wildlife hospital at Kapama where he would be nursed back to health. He would require antibiotics and careful monitoring after his operation in order to maximise his chances of survival.

The hyena had given up their quest once the reinforcements had arrived so now all that was required was to load the three hundred kilogram sleeping baby onto the back of one of the game vehicles and drive him to hospital. This required the efforts of all the people that were there that night. Two strong game rangers, two trackers and a vet. Once the baby was safely loaded, the journey back to the wildlife hospital started. This was not far as the crow flies but it was now pitch dark and the vehicles were off what little tracks there were. Adam took the lead and acted as a road maker. His driving ability through the bush was excellent. He chose the easiest routes that would also do the least damage to the bush. They arrived at the hospital and all hands were needed to once again lift the baby out of the transport vehicle. By this time

he was waking up. He was placed in a small enclosure that doubled as a hospital cage for small to medium sized herbivores. Peter decided to administer the antidote to the sedative and within a very short time of this injection the little rhino woke up. He took some tottering steps in his new enclosure. The evening was warm and it was felt that he would be safe enough here. He would still require regular feeding and a large bottle with a teat was used as he was still suckling. The nursing staff was roped in and a routine set up. They mixed and tested a milk formula and the little rhino seemed quite happy to drink this from a very large bottle with a teat specially designed for a baby rhino.

THE TWO OF THEM MADE A GREAT TEAM.

It took two weeks before the bandages were removed and to everyone's delight the wound healed beautifully. Lente Roode allowed the little rhino to live in one of the camps on the Cheetah Project and there he stayed for two years.

I met him when he had been there for about nine months and he must have weighed about six hundred kilograms. Another rescued rhino named Dave in honor of Prof Dave Meltzer was his companion. The two of them made a great team. They were not exactly tame but they were used to

humans to the point that if you approached them slowly
and carefully and talked all the while to them, they would
allow you to stroke them. This is a rare experience. They are
amazingly primitive to look at and their skin, whilst being very
thick, is also very sensitive. They can feel you stroking them

and actually seem to enjoy being scratched. Their heads are massive and can pivot amazingly. A rhino's neck is very short and the power that is generated by this fulcrum is awesome. If a rhino tosses its head and you happen to be in the way you will be seriously injured, if not by their horn then just by the sheer power generated by this movement.

The two rhinos responded when called. It was a great joy and also very amusing to stand alongside the fence and call them by name like you would a dog. A rhino's sight is poor and their memory is bad so if you don't talk to them all the time, they tend to forget that you are behind them. When they suddenly realise that you are behind them they take fright and that is when you can get bowled over by a six hundred kilogram rhino with all the consequent problems!

I had a number of amusing incidents with these two characters when I spent some time with them in their camps. It took me a while to pluck up the courage to stand in the camps by myself. Peter was used to their antics but I was still a bit nervous of these two large beasts. It takes a very brave or foolish person to just stand there when a pair of rhinos barrel up to you.

Eventually I got the hang of what to do and I realised that if you do exactly what you are told to do the chances of being hurt are small. On one visit we had one of our friends with us and unfortunately the rhinos decided to chase her. Although the event could have had serious consequences, it was really funny seeing this rather large lady leaping out of the way

MAYBE THAT WAS THE PuRPOSE INTENDED FOR MuNWANE.

and over the fence to try and escape from two really benign animals who just wanted to get to know her a bit better. But not such an amusing experience for our friend!

Adam came to see his rescued rhino on a regular basis and it was he who named him Munwane, which is a small river running close to where Adam found him. The relationship between the two of them was special. I don't know if Munwane had any knowledge that Adam had rescued him but the way that Munwane interacted with him was different to the way he behaved with anyone else. He became gentle and used to nuzzle Adam with what looked like affection.

At the end of the two-year period mentioned above, it was decided to allow the two rhino to join the main herd at Kapama. They lived there for a few months and then tragically Munwane was found dead. A poacher had killed him. His small horn had been cruelly hacked from his head and was probably sold to a muti shop for a paltry sum.

What price a life?

Adam was devastated by the news. He felt that he should never have intervened. Had the hyenas killed the rhino originally then at least some sort of natural cycle would have occurred.

I don't know what the answers are. All I know is that we do the best we can. Some we win and some we lose. The rescued rhino gave many people pleasure and everyone that came into contact with him and Dave came away just a little more sensitised to these marvelous primitive animals. Maybe that was the purpose intended for Munwane.

⊟ EPILOGUE ⊟

WE WERE IN A SMALL CLEARING WITH THE TRACKERS ABOUT TEN METERS AHEAD OF ME WHEN ALL HELL BROKE LOOSE. THE TRACKERS HAD STUMBLED ON TO NOT ONE BUT THREE LIONESSES AND THEY HAD CUBS.

Animals will usually run from man but a lioness with cubs will not. She will attack if she feels threatened and these three females with their cubs felt very threatened. They roared and snarled very loudly. It is impossible to do justice to the amount of noise they generated. There were waves of sound washing over us in deep base tones. The sound actually reverberated in our chests. I was terrified. Not for the first time I thought to myself that I should be sitting on my patio at my home in Cape Town sipping a drink and looking at the sea. What was I doing in the bush facing death? The prospect of being mauled to death by three angry lionesses loomed very large in my face.

But wait; possibly I should start at the beginning.

My name is Roy Aronson. I am a South African and a veterinarian. I qualified from vet school when I was in my late twenties and have been in private practice since then. It never ceases to amaze me just how many people wanted to be vets when they were young. Not many succeeded with their

IN ESSENCE, THIS IS AN AUTOBIOGRAPHY OF MY LIFE OVER SIX YEARS LOOKING THROUGH A FILTER

dream though. Only a select few have the privilege of actually training at a university and becoming vets. This book is about them. All vets have stories to tell; whether they work with large animals, small animals, wild animals or tame animals. They all have great stories to tell; the funny, happy, sad silly stories that happen to them in their daily lives. Their stories are the stuff that movies are made of, the stuff that books are written about. I have worked with many of them and these are their stories

I have many passions. Amongst these I am passionate about my profession and the great opportunities it has afforded me and I am passionate about this fantastic country that I live in. I have been fortunate enough to be able to combine my passions. A few years ago I had an idea about making a TV documentary. I would travel all over this wonderful land I live in, filming vets in action doing what both they and I love to do and that is heal animals large and small, wild and tame, beautiful and plain.

Whilst I was traveling to the various game reserves and visiting and working with different vets there was a subplot going on. This is the story behind the story. This was how persistence enabled me to maneuver myself into a position where the idea I had formulated could be translated into reality. The story about the connections I have made and the triumphs and disappointments that have marked my passage along the way. In essence, this is an autobiography of my life over six years looking through a filter that enables me to view only the salient pieces of my life associated with the pursuit of my dream.

I was involved with the team at Combined Artists, a production house that was originally going to produce the show. I was the presenter and originator of the idea. The executive producer of the show was George Mazarakis.

The executive producer is the person who not only shapes the show but also gets involved in raising finance. I too assisted in this function, but I was a complete unknown in the industry. I obviously had a good idea however because the idea actually attracted some powerful people who were influential in the movie industry.

One of the first things that we decided was to try and assemble a short promotional video that we could use to sell the show to a channel. With this in mind we went out and filmed the Gemsbok case, the fish with the bends, the hedgehog case, the reluctant bulldog mother and sexing of parrots. Using these five cases as well as some links we had filmed, we put together a short eight-minute promotional video. We met with the commissioning editors from M net, a pay for view channel in South Africa, and showed them our show. They loved it. The one commissioning editor had a bulldog and loved the case of the bulldog puppies being born by caesarian section.

We now had a broadcaster who would show the series once it was made but did not volunteer any money to make the show. We still needed a sponsor. For three years we went about trying to make contacts and raise funds

There were moments of excitement along the way but mostly I remember the disappointment and sadness when one after another of the contacts that we had so carefully nurtured turned us down or just ignored us.

A moment of great excitement was generated when one of the companies we approached agreed to sponsor the funding of the pilot. This was the Iams Company. They were a pet food manufacturer. I had approached the manager of the company in South Africa and he went to the USA and

WHAT WE DECIDED WAS
TO TRY AND ASSEMBLE A SHORT
PROMOTIONAL VIDEO

WE NOW HAD ASSEMBLED ENOUGH FOOTAGE TO TRY AND EDIT A DECENT PILOT.

pitched our product to the main board of the company. They donated a sum of money that enabled us to go out and shoot the pilot footage and edit it into a form that would give the viewers a solid taste of the show. We were assigned a producer who was to head the team. Once this was done, a small team comprising camera and sound men and producer and me, traveled into the bush to film some of the cases we were offered.

We had an opportunity to film a unique case of an adult leopard having a radio transmitter implanted into its abdomen. Unfortunately due to unfavorable circumstances, we missed this story. We had also tried to film the lion with its neck in the noose. We did not get the entire story on film and even though the actual story was a great one with a very good ending, we were not able to capture it then. We managed to obtain some footage that was useful but our main story was not completed and we went back to Johannesburg having spent a week in the bush without results. Within a short while we were once again called and we were offered the chance to film the story of Mehlwane, the lion with the entropion. We obtained a great story.

We now had assembled enough footage to try and edit a decent pilot. We selected the cases we wanted to show and after being briefed, the producers went into the edit suit with the editor and tried to put together the first episode. When this was done, we viewed the pilot but were disappointed. We felt that the ethos of the show was wrong. I spoke to the executive producer and we decided to try and re-edit the show

The executive producer and I did the edit this time. We finished our off line edit and then the on line editor took over and within a day we had a new pilot. This second offering was better than the first but still not quite what I had in mind.

Armed with this new offering, I once again tried to market the show. I plugged away for a further three years.

After this long and protracted period, I had the opportunity to visit my brother in the United States of America. I felt that it was an opportunity to try and further the cause of my show so before going, I contacted a good friend who was well connected in overseas markets. He managed to set up meetings for me with an associate of his in the movie industry in Los Angeles. Before leaving for the USA, I had my pilot transcribed into NTSC format, which is the television format in the USA. Armed with this and my proposals as well as my own talents and bush clothing, I flew to the USA.

I spent some time in New York and then went on to San Diego. Once there, I made contact with "my contact" and set up a meeting with him in Los Angeles. On the designated day I took a train from San Diego to Los Angeles. This is a great experience. The train travels along the west coast of the USA, literally. There are sections where there is just a narrow stretch of beach between the train and the sea. It is beautiful.

I arrived in LA and was fetched by a friend. My appointment was for a breakfast the next day so I had a chance to do some site seeing in LA. I was taken round and shown all the famous stars homes and the various places that are so frequently seen in the movies. It is an exciting city.

I SET uP A MEETING WITH "MY CONTACT" IN LOS ANGELES.

The next day I headed off for breakfast with John. We met at a hotel and I started to tell him who I was and what my show was about. I had a copy of my pilot, which I wanted to give him. He did not take it just then and asked me to meet with various people in the movie industry who were his contacts. Through a series of meetings I was able to accomplish in a few hours what many aspiring stars take a life time to do.

One meeting that amuses me when I think about it is the meeting I had with the head talent agent for the company Endevor Agencies. They had told me that I had fifteen minutes with him and his associate. I arrived at their offices dressed like

THEY ACTUALLY ENJOYED THE SHOW AND ALLOWED IT TO PLAY FOR ITS ENTIRE TWENTY MINUTES.

a fugitive from a safari movie. I had a khaki outfit on and wore a bush hat. I looked somewhat out of place for the middle of Los Angeles. I was kept waiting for the mandatory fifteen minutes then was rushed into an office with a large TV screen dominating the room. Next the busy and harassed executives came bustling in. Introductions were kept to a minimum and they started to ask me questions. I suggested that instead of spending our time talking they should view the pilot that I had brought with. This suggestion was accepted and the video was switched on and the cassette inserted and played.

The most amazing transformation then occurred. They both stopped talking and started concentrating. They actually enjoyed the show and allowed it to play for its entire twenty minutes. So much for the fifteen minute meeting. At the end of the show they peppered me with questions and at the end of an hour I was still with them.

"Jimmy" asked me when I was returning to South Africa. I told him I was scheduled to fly out the next day. He then called a senior executive at Fox TV studios and insisted that he see me that day. He convinced this person to see me by swearing at him profusely and telling him in a broad American accent that I "was the real thing from Africa dressed in Khaki". My appointment with the Fox executive was made for an hour later and Endevor was now officially representing me.

By the end of that day, I had acquired an agent in the USA and had met with the Fox executive and had all but signed a deal. This is the stuff dreams were made of. I had nearly made it in Hollywood; nearly, but not completely. Endevor are the largest independent agents in the USA. They had linked me up with a senior executive at Fox TV network who saw the show and loved it. They also linked me up with a company

called Weller Grossman who were a very big production house specializing in TV documentaries for may channels such as Discovery, National geographic, the Travel Channel, the History channel and others.

Gary Grossman loved my show and made many flattering remarks. They pitched the show to Discovery and we nearly had a deal.

I flew back to South Africa with the knowledge that I had an agent in the USA looking after my interests as well as some very influential people who wanted to make the show happen. By now I was even planning how I was going to spend all the dollars I was going to earn.

Then believe it or not, the second Iraq war broke out and all deals were suspended. Discovery backed out and Weller Grossman backed out as well. I could not believe just how fickle people can be. From hero to zero in the space of a heartbeat.

I could not believe my bad luck. We were so close to closing a deal that I was nearly spending my dollars. I felt totally defeated and dejected. The only thing that I still had was my perseverance. And this did not desert me just yet.

I had another friend who wanted to introduce me to two associates of his. They were local guys with an office close to where I lived in Cape Town. The irony did not escape me. I have traveled round the world trying to get my show done and then I am introduced to people who live round the corner. Maybe it was necessary in order to eventually get to this point.

It was at this point that the Imaginarium entered into the fray.

The Imaginarium is a production company run by two great guys; their headquarters were in Sea Point, really close to where I grew up. To me this was the ultimate irony. I had tried to peddle my product far and wide, from Johannesburg

THE SECOND IRAQ WAR BROKE OUT
AND ALL DEALS WERE SUSPENDED.

IT WAS DECIDED THAT WE WOULD GO OUT AND RE-SHOOT SOME LINKS AND REASSEMBLE THE PILOT.

to New York to Los Angeles and all the while, literally on my doorstep there was this company that has the ability and will to work with me.

Their first task was to get all legal documents in order. They wanted to know that I was the sole owner of the show. To this end I obtained signed documents from all the previous people I had worked with saying that they no longer had a stake in the show. Once this was obtained I was able to enter into a working agreement with the Imaginarium.

Chris was the creative partner and Issy was the financial brain. They had both watched version one of the pilot and whilst they accepted the quality of the footage they were unhappy about the quality of the production. It was decided that we would go out and re-shoot some links and reassemble the pilot.

Once this was done I once again hoped that we would be able to go out and sell the show to either a sponsor or a channel and then when we had the finance we would be able to make the show and fulfill what had now become a life obsession.

Once again my hopes were not fulfilled. Chris got involved in making a twenty six part science fiction film that took all his time and effort and Issy spent his time seeking funds for the show Chris was involved in and the same pattern repeated itself again. My show was once again sidelined.

By now I had spent the better part of six or seven years persuing a dream that I eventually realized would never be fulfilled. It was time to throw in the towel and give up.

And that is exactly what I did.

I had a large box of tapes; over sixty in all. We had actually filmed enough material for most of the show. I also had my diaries.

I had kept a diary of events and recorded all my adventures not only on film but also in writing. By the time I had finished I had what resembled a book of nearly two hundred pages. I read and re read my work and with the help of editors this is the only offering that I have to show for the years of hard work and dedication.

If however you have enjoyed reading my stories then I have achieved my dream beyond my wildest imagination because at the end of the day these years were about promoting my profession and my country and maybe this medium is after all the best way of doing that. Long after you have forgotten the movie, this small volume will still occupy a space on your bookshelf and you or your children will pick it up, page through it and derive pleasure and what more could I want from life than that.

Thank you for buying my book, thank you for reading my book. If you have really enjoyed it then all I ask of you is to tell your friends

Dr. Roy Aronson

November 2007

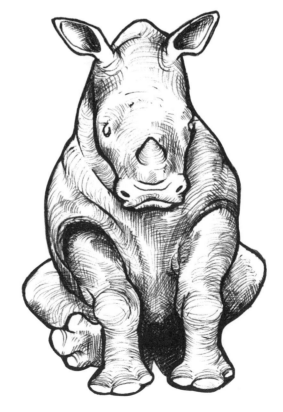

NOTES

 Tales of an African Vet